D1177359

...ntraub & Willis & I had lunch

...dsay, W. & I lunch

...wound on platinum mandrel

...between heated rolls

— — — — —

...aking

...d — a 9.8' mil fil. — had been drawn

...oll thru the metal to be rolled (400 - 500 amp)

...y

...s in Boston)

...g, swag'g & roll'g. ˄We perhaps should

of copper wire

BOOKS BY THE SAME AUTHOR

Master Builders of Sixty Centuries

Fares, Please!

Men and Volts at War

Workshop of Engineers

Modern Jupiter—the Story of Charles Proteus Steinmetz

At the Touch of a Button

Yankee Scientist

Photograph by Karsh, Ottawa

William David Coolidge

YANKEE SCIENTIST

William David Coolidge

BY JOHN ANDERSON MILLER

PUBLISHED BY
Mohawk Development Service
SCHENECTADY, NEW YORK

TK
140
C77
M64
1963

LP

COPYRIGHT © 1963 BY

MOHAWK DEVELOPMENT SERVICE, INC.

LIBRARY OF CONGRESS CATALOG CARD NUMBER 63-21209

All rights reserved. This book, or parts thereof,
must not be reproduced in any form without
permission of the publisher.

MANUFACTURED IN THE UNITED STATES OF AMERICA
BY THE MAQUA COMPANY

02/06/90

Foreword

William D. Coolidge came to the General Electric Research Laboratory in 1905, five years after its founding, and embarked upon a career that was destined to make his name famous the world over. Working side by side with Willis R. Whitney, he helped establish a pattern for doing scientific research in private industry which has had immeasurable impact on the subsequent growth of industrial research. His discoveries have had profound effect on the businesses of the General Electric Company and have contributed significantly to the welfare of humanity around the world.

A more modest man than Dr. Coolidge would be difficult to find. Once, upon accepting one of the scores of high honors which have been conferred on him, I heard him say, "Such honors as this I accept only if I can somehow share them with many others, since the entire staff of our research laboratory contributed to the success of this work."

Thus it is not surprising that Dr. Coolidge, as he reviewed the chapters of this biography, repeatedly expressed concern that "you make it sound too much as though I did it all myself, and so many others helped me who should be mentioned."

Our best reply is to express the belief that John Miller has done an admirable job of providing a well-balanced and objective summary of Dr. Coolidge's career. The words are laudatory because Dr. Coolidge is the kind of scientist—and the kind of man—who deserves the most sincere praise that his associates can express. Scientists in our own Research Laboratory and in many other laboratories throughout the world are indebted to him for wise counsel and inspiring leadership.

Guy Suits
Vice-President and Director of Research
General Electric Company

Schenectady, New York
September 1963

CONTENTS

1

Campus to Industry

"To the superficial mind, it may appear that we already know many of nature's secrets," William David Coolidge once said, "but he who looks deeper sees that in many cases we have hardly done more than to give names to her manifestations." No words could better characterize the outlook of today's scientist. He sees clearly what his counterpart of sixty years ago did not realize, that far more science is yet to be learned than has already been discovered.

Science in the early 1900's was neat and tidy. It was essentially factual. The phenomena of nature were explainable in terms of natural laws, most of which were regarded as fully established. Matter was believed to be made up of basic elements, of which there was a total of ninety-two. The acquisition of further knowledge seemed largely a question of filling in the details.

By the middle 1900's, science had ceased to be neat and tidy. A substantial number of its earlier principles had had to be discarded. Nobody knew exactly of what

1

matter was composed. The supposition was that it consisted of tiny particles—electrons and nucleons in continuous motion. The ninety-two basic elements had lost
much of their significance because it had been shown that
one element could be artificially changed into another.
Science had become a turbulent adventure, full of chal-
lenges and uncertainties. Its concept far transcended the
domain of measurable fact.

The ramifications of this change in outlook have been
tremendous, involving all scientists regardless of their
special fields. One of those who played a key part in
developing the new viewpoint was Dr. Coolidge who, for
twelve eventful years of this period of change was director
of the Research Laboratory of the General Electric Company and became one of the world's best known physical
chemists with honorary degrees from eight universities in
Europe, South America and the United States. For his
contributions to the progress of science, he received the
Rumford Medal of the American Academy of Arts and
Sciences, the Hughes Medal of the Royal Society of
England, the Faraday Medal of the Institution of Electrical Engineers of England, the Edison Medal of the
American Institute of Electrical Engineers and the Franklin Medal of the Franklin Institute, along with numerous
others. His own discoveries, in the words of the Franklin
Institute citation "have profoundly affected the welfare
of humanity." In addition, the Research Laboratory,
during the years under his direction, made many other
notable contributions.

That he would one day be cast in the role of head of a great industrial research organization would have seemed to Coolidge in his earlier years a pure fantasy. He was on the faculty of the Massachusetts Institute of Technology, busily engaged in studying the electrical conductivity of aqueous solutions at high temperatures. He liked the atmosphere of the Institute and was happy in his work. Before him stretched a vista of continued application to teaching and related research activity. Without warning, in the summer of 1905, he received a long-distance telephone call from his friend and former teacher, Dr. Willis R. Whitney. How would Coolidge like to leave the Massachusetts Institute of Technology, and become a member of the staff of the General Electric Research Laboratory at Schenectady?

The suggestion came as a complete surprise to Coolidge, who had never seriously considered taking a job in industry. His workroom at M.I.T. had adjoined Whitney's and they had often discussed the latter's new laboratory, but Coolidge had not thought of it in relation to himself.

Behind Whitney's invitation lay a curious situation. The carbon-filament electric lamp developed by Thomas A. Edison in 1879, which had been the foundation upon which the electrical industry had been built, was failing to meet the more exacting demands of the twentieth century.

"Too small, too red and too hot," was the way one critic described it. This seemed like rank heresy after Edison had made hundreds of experiments and spent a great deal of money in the successful development of the carbon filament. Edison, himself, is reported to have said in 1900 that the work done over the previous twenty years had so perfected the incandescent lamp that it was unlikely that it would ever be materially improved. But there were many who disagreed with Edison. They thought that lamps could be improved and set to work to do it.

One possibility seemed to be the radiant lamp in which an electric current passed through a long, thin, glass tube filled with a suitable gas. A lamp of this kind had been installed in the foyer of Madison Square Garden in New York City and had attracted a good deal of attention. Others were being installed elsewhere. They gave more light than the carbon-filament lamp for the same amount of energy. Though they were awkward to install and repair, they might pose a real threat to the conventional type of electric lamp. In Europe, scientists were experimenting with incandescent lamps having filaments of osmium, tantalum and tungsten. These, too, posed a threat to the carbon-filament lamp.

General Electric, as the leading manufacturer of carbon-filament lamps in the United States, had not remained idle under these conditions. Top executives had summoned Dr. Whitney, who was then in the process of building up the company's Research Laboratory, and assigned him the task of looking for a better material of which to make lamp filaments. A good man to work on this assignment, Whitney thought, would be his former student, Dr. William D. Coolidge, who was doing original research in physical chemistry at M.I.T.

The invitation to join the G.E. Research Laboratory staff put Coolidge in a quandary. The salary offered was twice the $1500 he was receiving as an assistant professor at M.I.T. This was important because he had incurred debts amounting to some $4,000 in securing his education. He was anxious to pay them off as quickly as possible. At the same time, he was very much interested in his M.I.T. studies of the electrical conductivity of aqueous solutions. He had great admiration for Whitney under whom he had studied chemistry as an undergraduate, but he was doubtful about transferring from the field of education to that of industry. Was industry really serious about going into research? The pioneer effort of the General Electric Company in setting up a research laboratory was still very young. Would the company be willing to continue spending money for research work where there was no certainty that it would result in increased profits? He was not interested in becoming a designer of improved commercial products; he was interested in the search for fundamental knowledge. He was concerned too, about the broad matter of academic freedom. Would he, in industry, have the same freedom to pursue studies of his choice that he enjoyed as a member of the M.I.T. faculty?

Coolidge explained these misgivings to Whitney, who understood them very well because he, himself, had had quite similar feelings when he had been asked to give up teaching at M.I.T. and organize the G.E. laboratory. Whitney assured Coolidge that the work he would do would, indeed, be fundamental research; and it would be done as nearly as possible in an academic atmosphere.

The General Electric Research Laboratory was something new, Whitney said. Organized scientific research was unknown in American industry before 1900. There were experimental laboratories in some of the larger plants, but these existed chiefly for the purpose of assisting the manufacturing processes. They were "trouble stations," called upon when something went wrong. Farsighted industrial leaders had begun to see that something more than this was needed. They realized that progress was built on increased knowledge. Men engaged constantly with the problems of manufacturing and selling had little or no time to study problems other than those arising in connection with their regular work.

The management of the General Electric Company had come to the conclusion that the greatest ultimate results would come from scientific pioneering which would open up broad new fields of knowledge, though it would not necessarily yield immediate financial returns. The company was not without its share of skilled engineers but they were occupied almost exclusively with the day to day problems of the company's operation. What was needed was a group of scientists who could work in comparative isolation from the activities of the factory, and free from interruption.

With this in mind, the company had, in 1900, decided to establish a research laboratory as a new component independent of all others. Whitney, who was already favorably known as a teacher of chemistry at M.I.T., had been asked to head it. This he had agreed to do with the understanding that such a laboratory would be given a free hand to pursue the acquisition of knowledge for its own sake. By 1905, the G.E. Research Laboratory was a going concern with a small but competent staff. Thus Whitney was able to reassure Coolidge on the matters that were troubling him, and persuade him to transfer his activities to Schenectady.

On September 11, 1905, Whitney wrote in his notebook, "Coolidge arrived to commence work."

REFERENCES

Coolidge, William D., "Autobiographical Notes," manuscript
————, "Formative Years of the Laboratory," Research Laboratory Colloquium paper, December 12, 1951
————, "The Role of Science Institutions in Our Civilization," Address at Ursinus College, October 13, 1942
Hammond, John Winthrop, *Men and Volts,* Lippincott, 1941
Langmuir, Irving, "Modern Concepts of Physics," Journal of American Chemical Society, 1929
Margenau, Henry, "The New Style in Science," Address at Rhode Island College, November 2, 1962
Searching Into the Unknown, General Electric Company, 1930

2

Family and Boyhood

Coolidge is one of the oldest names in New England. John and Mary Coolidge came over from England with Governor John Winthrop in 1630 and settled in Watertown, Massachusetts. Before crossing the ocean, they had lived at Cottenham in Cambridgeshire, where records of the family can be traced back to the 1300's. Various spellings of the name were used in early days—Cooledge, Cullege, Colledge, Cowlege and others. In America two spellings have been widely used, "Coolidge" and "Cooledge." The U.S. Census of 1790 shows twenty-five families in Massachusetts using the first of these spellings and ten using the second.

John Coolidge was a man of substance. He owned thirty acres at Watertown and was "Deputy to the Great and General Court of the Massachusetts Bay Colony." He had several sons who founded separate branches of the family in different parts of New England. For the most part, the Coolidges were not interested in becoming pioneers who opened up new territory. They were inclined to live in the general vicinity of Boston and the neighboring communities to the westward. One branch ventured a little farther and settled at Plymouth, Vermont.

William David Coolidge was born at Hudson, Massachusetts, October 23, 1873, the only child of Albert Edward Coolidge and Martha Alice Shattuck. Actually the records of the town clerk list his name as "Willie," though this was later changed to "William." He was the eighth generation of the family to be born in America, being descended from Simon, the second son of the original John and Mary. The Vermont Coolidges derived from this same branch, separating shortly after the Revolution.

Albert Edward was a farmer, as were a large proportion of the Coolidges. They were a tough-fibred and robust stock, living longer than most of their contemporaries. Conservative in viewpoint and reserved in manner, the Coolidges were substantial citizens who worked hard and paid their bills but did not, in the main, achieve special distinction. The notable exceptions were the original John, Calvin of the Vermont branch, who became the thirtieth President of the United States, and William David who attained world-wide fame as a scientist. Curiously, the latter two were born within a year of each other, Calvin being the older.

On one occasion in later years, William D. Coolidge, in company with several other G.E. men, had the privilege of being introduced to Calvin in the White House. He was immediately preceded in the line of visitors by Ray Stearns and, remembering that one of Cal's advisors was another Stearns, from Boston, they thought that Cal might possibly be amused on being introduced in rapid succession to Stearns and Coolidge; but if he was, he didn't show it.

Hudson, in 1873, was a town of about 3,500 people in Middlesex County. It lay somewhat west and a little south of Concord—near enough for its militia to have been called out on the nineteenth of April in 1775, and dispatched to the battles of Lexington and Concord. Boston was some twenty-eight miles distant. The literary atmosphere of Boston, Cambridge and Concord scarcely extended as far as Hudson. Its inhabitants were firm believers in education—its first schoolhouse was built in 1779 and its second in 1812—but its citizens did not write poetry and essays; some were farmers and others worked in the local factories.

The town had begun as a small group of houses in the vicinity of a dam across the Assabet River where a gristmill and a sawmill had been erected. Known first simply as "The Mills," it later became Feltonville and then Hudson. The Fitchburg Railroad, running from Marlboro to Boston had a station in Hudson. A round-trip ticket to Boston cost ninety cents. About the time of Coolidge's birth, a second railroad was built, the Massachusetts Central, joining Hudson with nearby communities.

Life in Hudson was much like that in other New England towns of comparable size. The original gristmill was still operating, but there were two sawmills in 1873 instead of one. There was a variety of other small manufacturing plants, too, for making bricks, carriages and sleighs, harness, curtains, light machinery, shoes, toys, pianos and melodeons. The town had three churches, a post of the Grand Army of the Republic and two temperance societies. Fire protection was provided by the Eureka No. 1 Hose Company. The inhabitants must have been of an easy-going temperament for the town directory listed three blacksmiths and six carpenters but only one lawyer.

One of the town's small business establishments had a particular fascination for Willie. This was the apothecary's shop. Whenever he had occasion to go there, he used to watch with rapt attention the process of pills being made up with a mortar and pestle. This was a kind of mechanical process with which he was to become thoroughly familiar later when he was experimenting with sintered tungsten.

The Coolidge farm was about a mile west of the center of Hudson in an area called Coolidgeville. Here numerous Coolidges lived in houses somewhat larger than those in the center of town and having more land around them. Willie's family kept a horse, a cow and a flock of chickens but the seven-acre farm was mostly given over to apple and peach trees, with part being reserved for a vegetable garden. As the farm was not particularly prosperous, Albert Edward worked most of the time in one of the local shoe factories. His wife augmented the family income by dressmaking. Though luxuries were largely absent, their boy had a happy childhood. As he, himself, said when a grown man, he never received anything but kindness, encouragement and help from his parents.

Willie Coolidge at the age of five

Farm life was austere in those days. There were no coal fires, running water, gas, electricity, telephones or radios, and, of course, no automobiles. As a boy, Coolidge was expected to do a few chores around the place, but not so many as he would have had to perform if the farm had had more livestock. Nevertheless, he usually put in an active day. He rose at six in the morning in a room which was, in winter, both cold and dark. He dressed by the light of an oil lantern and washed in cold water in the kitchen. After breakfast he walked about a mile to the nearest school. This was a pleasant walk in warm weather, but rather rugged when snow lay knee-deep on the ground.

The school building was a one-room affair which housed the first six grades, all presided over by one woman teacher. The pupils covered a wide range of ages. They were, to a large extent, dominated by a group of the older boys, some of whom were quite big and strong. On one occasion a group of them put the teacher in the wood-box, closed the cover and sat on it. No harm was meant it was just horseplay. The boys were mischievous, but not malicious.

Despite the disparity in ages, the pupils got on well together. Though quiet and rather reserved in manner, Coolidge was well-liked by his fellow students, who generally called him "Will." One of the pupils was a negro boy, who was as popular as anybody. Lunches were carried to school in collapsible metal boxes. During the mid-day recess the bread they contained was often toasted at the end of a pointed stick before the fire in the wood stove.

Smoking was, of course, strictly forbidden. The pupils, indeed, had no opportunity to buy tobacco. But smoking has always had a strong attraction for school boys. When the teacher was temporarily out of the room, the boys used to break off pieces of her rattan wastebasket and use them as cigarettes. Careful selection of the places to break off the pieces permitted the practice to go undetected for a long while. When it was necessary the teacher used the ruler vigorously on the hands of refractory pupils. Serious misbehavior was punished by sending the culprit to be reprimanded by a member of the School Committee.

By modern standards this school would surely be rated as primitive. But Coolidge liked the teacher and was interested in what he was taught. Because of the competition of one very bright girl in the class, he worked harder than he would otherwise have done.

Fishing was a popular sport among the boys of the village. This was a year-round activity. The fish were not safe even when, as Thoreau of nearby Concord describes it, winter drew "an icy curtain over their broad skylight." The boys simply chopped holes through the ice, and continued their fishing. The holes were about eight inches in diameter. A baited line was dropped through the hole and provided with a telltale flag device on the surface of the ice. When a fish took the bait the flag snapped up to a vertical position so that it could be seen from some distance. A fisherman on skates could serve as many as twenty lines. The boys did not actually catch a great many fish, but success rewarded their efforts just often enough for the pastime to seem worthwhile. For use on snow, Coolidge and his boyhood friends did not have real skis, but instead they used barrel staves to each of which a portion of an old shoe was attached.

After finishing grade school, Coolidge attended Hudson High School. He enjoyed all of his work there except the exercises in elocution. Getting up before the class to recite a bit of poetry or prose was very distasteful to him. He minded this so much that his father arranged for him to take private lessons in elocution. These gave him more confidence and were very helpful.

Willie's early hobbies included baseball and photography. He built a darkroom in the basement of the farmhouse and constructed his own camera, including the shutter. To lessen the discomfort of getting up on a cold winter morning, he devised a contraption that would, at a pre-set time, ring an alarm, close the open window of his bedroom and open the door into the hall to admit heat from the warmer part of the house. He also built an electric motor to drive the sewing machine his mother used in her dressmaking business. Unfortunately this motor would not run, though what was wrong he never discovered.

When partly through high school, Willie decided that he should be making some contribution to the family income. He, therefore, stopped going to school and took a job with the Apsley Rubber Company. His work there consisted in folding rubber raincoats for shipment from the factory to retailers. This job was of short duration and was followed by work as assistant to the bookkeeper. After a few months, however, Coolidge decided that leaving school had been a mistake, and that he should go back. As a good part of the time he had been working was during the summer, he was able to rejoin his class without any serious handicap.

Because he liked his studies and applied himself industriously to them, he did extremely well at high school. When graduation came around, he stood number one in a class of thirteen and was chosen valedictorian. The subject of his discourse was "Life is Opportunity."

This he expected to be the end of his educational career as family finances did not extend to providing tuition at college. But one day a friend who knew of his interest in mechanical and electrical devices, suggested that with his excellent scholastic record, he might get a state scholarship for tuition at the Massachusetts Institute of Technology. He applied and was successful. The early fall of 1891 saw him headed for Boston and M.I.T. to continue his studies.

REFERENCES

Coolidge, Emma D., *Descendents of John and Mary Coolidge of Watertown, Massachusetts,* 1930

Coolidge, William D., "Autobiographical Notes" manuscript

Haynes, Mrs. Norma, Librarian, Hudson Public Library, unpublished letter

Kent, Mrs. Howard N., Concord Antiquarian Society, unpublished letter

Mayo, Mrs. Howard A., President, Hudson Historical Society, unpublished letter

O'Mallay, A. J., Town Treasurer, Hudson, Mass., unpublished letter

3

Student at M.I.T.

When the train from Hudson deposited young Will Coolidge at the Fitchburg Railroad Station in Boston, he found himself on unfamiliar ground. He had been to the city a couple of times before on one-day excursions, but these trips had given him only small glimpses of this metropolis with half a million inhabitants. The sidewalks swarmed with people and the pavements swarmed with vehicles. Above the roadway ran the newly-built elevated railway. Boston had at that time the largest street railway system in the world, and the group of three railroad stations standing side by side on Causeway Street, called "Railroad Row," was one of its focal points. Will had never seen greater congestion.

The Massachusetts Institute of Technology, then generally called "Boston Tech," was located on Boylston Street, not far from Copley Square. This was a residential neighborhood about a mile or so from the station. Young Coolidge was accustomed to walking considerable

17

Will Coolidge when he entered M.I.T.

distances in the country, but he had luggage to carry, and he took a streetcar from the station, changing at Tremont House to the line that ran out Boylston Street.

After reporting to the registrar, Will sought out the place where he was going to live for the next eight months. Boston Tech had no dormitories to accommodate its students. Some lived at home in Boston and surrounding towns. A small fraction lived in fraternity houses. A few commuted by railroad from places as far away as Providence, Taunton and Plymouth. Though Hudson was nearer to Boston than were these places, Coolidge did not undertake to commute. Like the majority, he took lodgings in the neighborhood of the school. He selected a rooming house a few blocks away on Beacon Street where he and another student shared a room on the fourth floor back.

In the 1890's most of the activities of Boston Tech were concentrated in three buildings. Of these, the most imposing was the Rogers Building, completed in 1866 and named in honor of William Barton Rogers, first president of the Institute. This was a four-story red brick and sandstone structure of classical design with a wide flight of granite steps. At the time it was built, it was the "last structure west on Boylston Street." Alongside the Rogers Building was the Walker Building, completed in 1883 and named for General Francis Amasa Walker, third president. It, too, was of red brick, but its severely plain exterior was in sharp contrast with the pleasing architecture of the building with which it shared the grounds. The

third building, completed in 1888, was a six-story structure on Trinity Place known as the Engineering Building.

Although Boston Tech had no facilities for housing its
students, it did provide a cafeteria-type lunchroom in the
basement of the Rogers Building. Its facilities were used
by both faculty and students. Will had many a meal here
during his college course. The room was a pleasant place,
and the meals were extremely good. A typical menu of the
1890's included pea soup, clam chowder, boiled halibut,
baked beans, brown bread and cold corned beef. The
price of a hearty meal was 25 to 35 cents.

The educational policy of the Massachusetts Institute
of Technology was unique for those days. Its founding
coincided with a period of rapid development of science
and technology in the United States. Boston was a great
center of both industry and capital. Popular interest in
science was growing rapidly. William Rogers and his
brother Henry had conceived the idea of a new type of
education that would provide for industry directive power
to utilize this new knowledge of science and supply the
higher technical skills now needed. Boston seemed like
the best place to locate a school of this kind. Engineers
were much in demand, but few were available. Most of
them were self-taught as the only institution of learning
which included engineering in its curriculum was the
United States Military Academy at West Point. Many
West Point graduates resigned from the army after a few
years to practice civil engineering, but this number was
nowhere near enough to meet the demand.

After years of hard work, public meetings, discussions and arguments in the newspapers, the Rogers brothers persuaded the State of Massachusetts to grant a charter to the Massachusetts Institute of Technology. Its aims were, as stated in its first catalog, printed in 1865:

> First — to provide a full course of scientific studies and practical exercises for students seeking to qualify themselves for the professions of the Mechanical Engineer, Civil Engineer, Practical Chemist, Engineer of Mines, and Builder and Architect,
>
> Second — To furnish such general education, founded upon the Mathematical, Physical and Natural Sciences, English and other Modern Languages, and Mental and Political Science, as shall form a fitting preparation for any of the departments of active life; and—
>
> Third—To provide courses of Evening Instruction in the main branches of knowledge above referred to, for persons of either sex who are prevented, by occupation or other causes, from devoting themselves to scientific study during the day, but who desire to avail themselves of systematic evening lessons or lectures.

The first two years of the curriculum were the same for all students, while the third and fourth years were devoted to professional studies. Military training was part of the curriculum from the earliest days. This was required under the federal Land Grant Act by which the original establishment of M.I.T. had been partly financed.

Thus the philosophy of the Institute was basically to furnish an education that would be of practical use to its graduates. At the same time President Rogers was firmly of the opinion that engineering training should be combined with sufficient cultural subjects to provide a sound education. Courses in literature, philosophy and modern languages had to be taken by all students.

Eventually, M.I.T.'s philosophy concerning scientific education was to be adopted by other schools. Its aim was practical—to help solve the great industrial problems of the times—but not wholly materialistic. As President Elliot of Harvard once said to a gathering of technical graduates "The human imagination is as much to be used in science as in poetry or the drama—a form of imagination as searching, as powerful, as any other form of human imagination. The occupations to which you are devoted, to which your successors are to be devoted, are not to be thought of as materialistic only. They have their feet on the ground, but their heads are in the sky."

As a boy, Will Coolidge had been interested in both mechanical and electrical things. When the time came to select his college course, he chose electrical engineering. This course had been added in 1882. Chemistry was one of the subjects included in it. Here he came under the instruction of Professor Willis R. Whitney, himself an M.I.T. graduate of a few years earlier. This was the start of a long and intimate association that played a major part in shaping Coolidge's career.

Whitney had a tremendous interest in fundamental science. His belief, as he once expressed it, was that "Discovery and invention are not terminals; they are fresh starting points from which we can climb to new knowledge." This philosophy was of even greater value to his students than the chemistry he taught them.

Another of Coolidge's instructors was Professor Goodwin, head of the physics laboratory. One day Will brought to him a question about the volume change taking place in a liquid when a soluble salt is added to it. Goodwin carefully explained that this might result in either an increase or a decrease in the volume of the liquid. The professor's detailed and enthusiastic discussion of the subject made a lasting impression on his young questioner.

Commenting on the incident many years later, Coolidge said, "I think his response to my question was, in no small measure, responsible for my later desire to do graduate work in science. It helped by increasing my interest in fundamentals. It might not have been as helpful had it been forced feeding; but it wasn't; it was something I had asked for. The value of an enthusiastic teacher can't be overestimated."

Everyday expressions that we hear and use without second thought often provide a clue to an important truth. "I get the idea," or "I see what you mean," or "Light dawns" are examples of this. Taken literally, they indicate only that the speaker now understands what you are explaining to him. But, actually, they convey more than that; they disclose the real pleasure and satisfaction of the speaker in receiving an understandable explanation of something about which he has been curious.

Because Coolidge, himself, appreciated a good explanation, he always tried to make his own explanations adequate and understandable. "He has always been extremely liberal of his time when talking with others and answering their questions," said a fellow scientist who had known him for many years.

Social activities and athletics played small parts in the lives of Boston Tech boys in the 1890's. There was, in fact, little time available for these diversions. The schoolwork was laid out for eight hours a day, six days a week. This included a great deal of laboratory work. Then, too, the Institute operated a carpenter, blacksmith and welding shop a few blocks away on Garrison Street. Here the students learned at first hand to make some of the devices studied in their engineering courses.

There were some intramural football games and occasional athletic contests with other schools. A certain amount of exercise was obtainable in a nearby armory which was used as a gymnasium as well as for the required military drill. Uniforms and rifles were provided, and an officer of the United States Army acted as instructor. Periodic drills were held, and once in a while, the unit took part in a parade.

One of the armory's few items of gymnastic equipment was a large rope suspended from the roof. Will Coolidge soon acquired considerable proficiency in pulling himself up, hand over hand, to the top of the rope. This exercise had a sequel that nearly ended in disaster.

Will and his roommate, living on the top floor of a fairly old building, felt that they should have an emergency fire escape. They bought a coil of rope, one end of which they proposed to make fast in the room, while the other was thrown out of the rear window to provide means of reaching the ground if fire cut off the stairway.

Late one night after he had completed his studies, Will decided to test the new fire emergency equipment. He pushed his desk close to the open window, and tied one end of the rope around the desk. Then he climbed out of the window and started to slide down as he had so often slid down the rope at the armory.

But this experiment had not been thought through with sufficient care. The rope was too small, and his hands began to slip. He tried to wrap his legs around the rope, but could not manage it. For four full stories, he slid down the rope holding it as tightly as he could with his hands. By the time he reached the ground, the flesh was hanging in shreds on the fingers of both hands. Late as it was, he managed to find a doctor after some search. The doctor bandaged Will's hands but he used as a disinfectant a carbolic acid solution that was too strong. This took off what skin remained on the fingers and palms of his hands.

The whole episode was very painful, and was specially troublesome because it took place only a short time before a period of written examinations. Will indulged in a good deal of self recrimination, telling himself that he should have known enough to start at the bottom instead of the top. Then, when he found the rope was too small, he would have been only a few feet above the ground, and could have slid down this short distance without harm and then knotted the rope for another attempt.

To make matters worse, the story of his escape from a non-existent fire got into a Boston newspaper for all his friends and acquaintances to read. This, plus the very noticeable bandages, provided his classmates with plentiful material for ribbing him. Eventually, the injured hands recovered, but the scars remained permanently.

During the summer vacation between his third and fourth years, Will took a temporary job at the East Pittsburgh plant of the Westinghouse Electric Company. This gave him valuable knowledge of electrical manufacturing processes. It also demonstrated the value of the fundamental studies at Boston Tech as they enabled him to understand the whys and wherefores of the design of electric equipment of types with which he had not had previous experience.

The news of Roentgen's discovery of x-rays created a great stir in scientific circles during the winter of 1895–1896. It was discussed with much interest by the students and faculty at M.I.T., and a certain amount of experimental work was carried out. No one was more keenly interested in this subject than Will Coolidge. He absorbed every bit of information he could get about it. During the following summer, he built at home a good-sized electrostatic machine with which he made a number of x-ray experiments. Most of the construction work was done in a small machine shop operated by one of his father's friends in Hudson. Later he sold the machine to a local doctor for x-ray work.

Although Will had entered the Institute as a member of the class of 1895, he had been forced to drop out a year on account of illness, and he graduated as a member of the class of 1896. Early in June of that year, he received from the dean the precious notice "I take pleasure in informing you that you have been recommended by the faculty for the degree of Bachelor of Science."

On Tuesday, June 9, graduation exercises were held in Huntington Hall. President Walker opened the program with an explanation of the scope of the theses that had been prepared by the members of the class. Representative abstracts were read by graduates from each course in the Institute. This was followed by the President's address and the conferring of 192 degrees, making 1896 the largest graduating class up to that time. Will Coolidge tucked his degree under his arm and returned to Hudson.

Despite the financial help obtained through his scholarship, he had gone considerably into debt to finance his education up to this point. For this reason, he did not plan to take up post-graduate studies as did some of his classmates. Nor was he inclined to go into industry. "My Pittsburgh experience," he once remarked, "was far from being a romantic one." Instead, he decided to take a position as assistant in physics at M.I.T. This would permit him to remain in the academic atmosphere which he had found very attractive during his undergraduate years.

One day after his return to M.I.T. in the fall of 1896, a friend suggested the possibility of Will's getting a fellowship that would enable him to undertake post-graduate study in Europe. This seemed like a good idea, and he put in his application. When his application was approved, he selected the University of Leipzig, which was famous throughout Europe as a center of scientific work. In this decision he was influenced in part by a desire to study physics under Leipzig's renowned Professor Paul Drude, and in part by the fact that his former chemistry teacher at M.I.T., Professor Whitney, had done post-graduate work at Leipzig.

As soon as the spring term ended at the Massachusetts Institute of Technology, Will Coolidge set out for Europe. An uneventful trip by train to New London, Conn., and thence by steamer down Long Island Sound, landed him at New York City on the morning of June ninth. There he spent a day whose program foreshadowed many days that were to come during the next two years.

Carrying his heavy suitcase, he walked from the dock up to Broadway and inquired for a room at the Hotel St. Denis. Finding that this would cost more than he wanted to pay, he politely withdrew and continued along the street until he came to the Broadway Central Hotel where he obtained a room at a rate of three dollars per day.

As the ship which was to take him to Europe was not scheduled to sail until the following day, he started on a tour of the city. Grant's Tomb was his first objective. He found it impressive, but did not linger long. From there he proceeded to the Metropolitan Museum of Art. He considered the paintings and statues there "the finest I have ever seen." Next he looked over the Central Park Zoo, and thence by the "El" to Battery Park where he gazed across the harbor at the Statue of Liberty. From lower Manhattan he took a ferry across the east River to Brooklyn, getting a good look at the Brooklyn Bridge on the way. After dinner he wandered up and down the Bowery for a while to see another aspect of the life of the city. Even with twentieth century transportation facilities this would be a large territory to cover in a single day of sight-seeing. With the slower streetcars and elevated railways of the 1890's it was an amazing feat.

On the following morning, he crossed the Hudson River by ferry to Hoboken and the North German Lloyd pier from which his ship, the *Barbarosa,* was to sail. But he found she had been delayed in arriving and would be a day late in sailing. This gave him additional time for sight-seeing and he started on a tour of Hoboken. There he found little of interest except Steven's Castle, for many years the home of Stevens Institute of Technology, standing on a bluff overlooking the river. Along the waterfront to right and left of the *Barbarosa's* pier stretched a long line of docks of other steamship lines. His walk, while of only moderate interest, gave him a chance to buy a dozen lemons which, he had been told, were a good precaution against seasickness.

That night he slept aboard the *Barbarosa,* which put to sea at noon the following day. His cabin, in the second class section of the ship, was small but comfortable enough. Virtually all of his fellow passengers were Germans. This pleased him greatly because of the opportunity it offered for him to practice the language. Having studied German at M.I.T., he got along well enough though not exactly with fluency.

Beautiful weather delighted the passengers at the beginning of the trip. On the second day out, however, the ship ran into a storm which caused a good deal of pitching and rolling. Will then learned that lemons are not a sure preventive of seasickness.

The storm ended after a couple of days, the sun came out and the passengers' appetites returned. The ever-changing pattern of the waves fascinated Will and he spent some of his time photographing them. Land was sighted on June twentieth, and a little later the *Barbarosa* put into Southampton harbor. Here an astonishing sight met his eyes. What seemed to be the whole of the Royal Navy was anchored there in preparation for the Queen's Jubilee. Nearly two hundred ships were drawn up in three lines which extended for miles. The United States was represented by its newest battleship, the U.S.S. *Brooklyn.*

From Southampton the *Barbarosa* proceeded to Bremerhaven, where Will went ashore. After spending a few hours sight-seeing in the city of Bremen, he took the night train for Leipzig, arriving there at eight o'clock in the morning of June twenty-third.

REFERENCES

Broderick, John T., *Willis Rodney Whitney,* Fort Orange Press, 1945

Coolidge, William D., "Autobiographical Notes," manuscript

———, unpublished letters from Leipzig

Driscoll, James, unpublished recollections of M.I.T. in the 1890's

Forty-five Year History of the Class of 1896 M.I.T., 1942

Prescott, Samual C., *When M.I.T. was "Boston Tech,"* The Technology Press, 1954

Taylor, John Bellamy, unpublished recollections of M.I.T. in the 1890's

4

Two Years in Europe

"I am in tip-top condition," Will Coolidge wrote to his parents shortly after his arrival in Leipzig. This was to become a familiar theme in his correspondence with them. Sometimes he was "in A-1 shape," but no matter how strenuous his activities on the previous day, each morning found him chipper as a lark. The pace he set himself in work and play was a continuing source of astonishment to his friends, but he seemed to thrive on it.

Leipzig was one of the largest and most important universities in Germany. Its buildings were handsome and impressive. It had nearly 4000 students and a faculty of about 200 members. This was far bigger than M.I.T. which had about 1200 students in those days. At Leipzig, as at other European universities, no dormitories were provided to house the students. The general practice was for them to take lodgings in the homes of townspeople living near the university.

Will's first lodgings were in the home of a Frau Schmit on Georgen Strasse. Even before he had established himself there, George Wendell, a friend of M.I.T. days took him to see Professor Gustav Wiedemann, head of the university's physics department. The latter advised him not to register formally at the university until October when the fall term began. For the time being, said Professor Wiedemann, Herr Coolidge could attend his physics lectures free of charge. This seemed like a good suggestion, and Will decided to follow it. These lectures were given six days a week, and the day following his arrival at Leipzig found him in attendance.

To improve his knowledge of the German language, he decided to stay away from the English and Americans in Leipzig as much as possible and mix with the Germans. He even attended German church services. This careful planning was a characteristic of his activities throughout his stay in Europe. "I have chewed this over in my mind," is a statement that appears frequently in his letters to his parents.

When Professor Weidemann's course of lectures came to an end in the middle of the summer, Will took a six-week trip to the Hartz Mountains so that he could see something more of the country and observe German customs and dress. As in New York, he did a lot of energetic sight-seeing, visiting historic buildings, stores, markets and other places of interest.

During part of his trip, he lodged with a family named Pilling at Schleusingen. Here he had an opportunity to improve his ability to speak German, while some of the natives sought to polish up their own knowledge of English. "It's enough to make a cat laugh," Will told his father and mother, "to hear some of them try to say a few words in English." But he was diplomatic; he complimented them on each recognizable attempt.

Coolidge's own linguistic progress was steady, but he sometimes found himself out of his depth. On August twenty-third he wrote to his parents. "I'm having a remarkable opportunity to learn German. Last night I went down to supper at 7:00 and came back to my room at 9:50. I read aloud to Herr P. and then talked X-rays to him." But in the same letter he says "I went to church yesterday morning, but couldn't understand the sermon."

His pronunciation was at times less good than his knowledge of the words. In one letter he says "I made a bull a few days ago. I said to Frau Pilling in the presence of her daughter 'Es ist gut Sport zu angeln fur Forellen.' (It is good sport to fish for trout.) My pronunciation was so bad that they understood it, 'Es ist gut Sport zu angeln fur eine fräulein.' (It is good sport to fish for a Fräulein). Hully gee!"

One significant result of this Hartz Mountain trip was Will's making the acquaintance of a Dr. Chamizer, a resident of Leipzig and the literary manager of the publishing house of Drugulin and Company. The doctor was a great linguist and had corrected proofs of editions of the Bible in more than twenty different languages.

A friendship quickly sprang up between the young American student and the doctor. When Coolidge returned to the city he "chewed it over" and decided that he would learn German most quickly if he lived with a large family such as the Chamizers where there would be a great deal of conversation.

"About noon I started out to call on my friend Dr. Chamizer," he wrote to his family on September eighteenth. "He finally consented to take me in. I'm living in his library, which contains at a guess, 2000 volumes. I shalln't read many of these books as they're nearly all in Hebrew, Arabic, Latin, etc. Near a big double window stands my roll-top desk. The room contains also a lounge, a table and a splendid porcelain stove. My bed is in an alcove which is separated from the room by draperies. Then, just outside the door I have a big wardrobe all to myself. I can develop pictures here to my heart's content. One of the boys has a little camera and we shall work together in the dark room. I eat with the family, which comprises two boys and two girls. Then there are three other boarders who have been here now for five years. The older daughter, Betty, is perhaps twenty one, dark complexioned and rather pretty. But the mother is the most attractive feature—she is, judging from a short acquaintance, just about as nice as could be . . . The price is all right—twenty dollars per month for everything except my washing. That includes service, light and fire. I rather guess the food is going to be all right—she makes elegant cocoa for me mornings and afternoons. I've told her how I like it and she makes it just right . . . I can go into the sitting room every afternoon and talk as much as I want to—there's sure to be someone there."

Before his arrival in Leipzig he had always pictured himself living in a garret and poring over books without a single thing to distract him. The reality proved quite different.

The work at the university began in earnest in October. The matriculation ceremonies included shaking hands with the president of the institution and receiving an identification card. This gave the student the privilege, if arrested, of being disciplined by the university rather than the city law enforcement agencies. It also permitted the purchase of theater tickets at half-price. At the same time Will lost a privilege "If I should marry while attending the university," he told his parents, "they'd kick me out."

Coolidge took a project with Professor Drude measuring the dielectric constant, temperature coefficient and absorption of various liquids. His daily program was to arrive at the university at 8 A.M. to hear a lecture by Drude on electricity and magnetism, and then to spend two hours in his own little laboratory working on his project. This was followed by a lecture on mathematics. After that he went home for lunch and returned to spend the whole afternoon in his laboratory until six or seven o'clock. On Mondays and Wednesdays he also attended lectures on radiation phenomena. He had little difficulty understanding most of the lectures, his main problem being those on mathematics, where the lecturer spoke too fast for him.

One aspect of his project pleased him very much; the apparatus for conducting his experiments was complete.

No time was wasted constructing it, or making modifications in what was in existence in order to serve a special purpose.

Drude used to visit Coolidge in the latter's small laboratory every morning after the lecture on electricity and magnetism. He would take a couple of thin slices of black bread out of his pocket and eat them while he listened to an account of the progress of the project. Professor Wiedemann used to drop in once a week for an informal chat. Will did not learn any physics during Wiedemann's visits, but he gained practice, he says, in the art of understanding a joke in a foreign language.

November twelfth proved to be a red letter day. Professor Drude brought into the laboratory a complete set of wireless telegraph instruments. Herr Coolidge was invited to inspect them. He was greatly impressed, but he told his family "With the Doctor's x-ray machine (in Hudson) I could do the same thing. When I come home I think I'll have to establish telegraphic communications between our house and the doctor's."

Shortly before Christmas a reception was held in commemoration of the fiftieth anniversary of Professor Wiedemann's receiving his doctorate. This was an important occasion with a long list of distinguished guests. Formal attire was, of course, necessary. Will had no clothes of this kind, and was living on a very modest budget. He was reluctant to spend the money to purchase them, but felt he had to do so. So he bought himself a dress suit, a silk hat and a pair of kid gloves. He attended the reception and

Herr Coolidge at Leipzig

found it extremely interesting. "I felt pretty spruce with a silk hat," he told his parents. "I think it's quite becoming. It's a nice-looking hat, too. That's pretty cheap—$2.00— for a tall hat with a case for it and a little velvet cushion for brushing it."

Despite a lot of hard work at the university, Will remained in "A-1 condition." He continued to write regularly to his family, but not quite so frequently as at first. He took short bicycle trips for exercise whenever he could find the time. For amusement, he was teaching the older Chamizer girl to speak English, and the older boy to take and develop photographs.

On one occasion the Chamizer boy took a snapshot of Will standing in the garden and wearing his best grey suit. When Will saw the print of this picture, he decided it was high time he had the suit pressed.

Amid his many activities, Will maintained an interest in the electrostatic machine he had built and sold to his friend, the doctor in Hudson. "Does it seem to work just as slick as it did when it was new?" he asked his mother. "I'd just like it here in my room," he continued. "It's really strange what a fascination such a machine has for me—I never tire of them. I have already begun to look forward with the greatest pleasure to the time when I can build a still larger one for my room."

With an abrupt change of subject he added, "I forgot to tell Betty not to wake me up at the usual hour tomorrow, so she'll get me up at 7:15 A.M. That's a mighty early son-rise for Leipzig on Sunday."

Coolidge always tried to live as economically as possible. His board and lodging at the Chamizers were very
moderate in cost. He was extremely careful of expendi-
tures on his sight-seeing trips. But some money had to be
spent on clothes.

"To my sorrow," he told his mother and father, "my
grey trousers (in the seat) have become transparent not
only to Roentgen rays but also to ordinary light, and are
at present at the tailors being put in wearing condition.
If they look too badly to wear to school, I shall use them
only in my Arbeit room."

Spring vacation afforded an opportunity for a quick
trip to Italy, a good part of which was spent in Florence.
As on previous trips he covered a good deal of ground in
the time available. But his sight-seeing was by no means
superficial. His power of observation was extremely acute,
and he gave careful thought to what he saw.

On March 27 he wrote from Florence:

"Have spent a busy day—it's Sunday & for that reason
entrance has been free to all of the various collections—
so I've *hustled*. This morning I took a walk—an appetizer
—went through the terrace garden (public) which is built
on a steep side hill. The garden is in itself, with its lovely
walks and charming grottoes, well worth seeing and the
view of Florence which it affords is magnificent. Snow had
fallen on the tops of the surrounding mountains during
the night and these snow caps sparkling in the morning
sun added much to the charm of the picture. Leaving the
gardens and continuing my walk up the hill I passed an

old cloister and came finally to a pretty little church and a graveyard. The latter was interesting—a more beautiful one I have never seen excepting perhaps 'Mt. Hope' and 'Mt. Auburn'—and these in some respects do not compare with this one here. In many instances, on the family lot stood a little chapel in stone & very often in white marble. The windows of these little chapels or tombs (as we must call them) were often painted like ordinary church windows and in some cases there were beautiful stone mosaics in the gables.

"After this tour, I breakfasted at my hotel and went to the Uffizi Gallery—my original intention was to slip right through this but the temptation to drop in for a minute and see a few of my favorites was too great so I stayed here a little while and then I went to the *Pitti*. Here I saw some paintings that I can never forget. For me, *the painting* in Florence is one of the several Madonnas by Raphael in the Pitti Gallery—a picture of such exquisite feminine beauty I have never seen before. A Madonna by Titian, also in the Pitti, was another source of great attraction for me. But such things are to be *seen* and not to be *described*.

"Then I made a hurried visit to the National Museum where I saw, besides a pair of statues by Michelangelo, little of interest to me. Then I made a flying visit to St. Mark's Museum where I saw a lot of beautiful frescoes. Then I came back and had some dinner at the hotel—by this time it was 5 P.M. but I was not very tired and decided to take a nice little walk to a neighboring town."

Back in Leipzig once more he plunged into his academic work with characteristic vigor. Professor Drude told him "I have never seen anyone as zealous as you are." In June, he came to the conclusion that he had accidentally hit upon a new method of showing electrical waves on wires. Drude was tremendously interested, sometimes coming to Coolidge's laboratory several times in a single day to watch the progress of this experiment. Will thought he might take this on as a little project in addition to his main project.

Prior to this, it had been possible to make such demonstrations on wires only in a long glass vacuum tube. Will found, however, that it could be done out in the open air, in a darkened room, if the wires were sufficiently small in diameter and the wave source were powerful enough. This was something quite new and he was asked to demonstrate it at the annual meeting in Dusseldorf of the German Natural Scientists and Doctors in the fall of 1898. In anticipation of the event, the old grey suit was discarded and a new one purchased as near as possible like it.

As the equipment was a bit complicated and had to be set up and adjusted on a lecture table shared with other speakers, and as this was to be his first lecture in the German language, and before an audience containing some of Germany's greatest physicists, the assignment proved quite worrisome. Fortune, however, smiled on him, the demonstration was successful and the audience seemed appreciative. After the nerve-wracking ordeal was over, Drude took Will to dinner. "It was a fine feed," Will commented. The paper was published in the *Annalen der Physik und Chemie,* and a German instrument-making company later put this type of equipment on the market.

In the interval between the discovery of this new demonstration method and the presentation at Dusseldorf, Coolidge spent his summer vacation touring the Rhineland, mostly by bicycle. This was his favorite method of locomotion and he liked to go as fast as he could. "If Herr Coolidge should go on the race track," a friend once remarked, "none of Leipzig's racers would have any chance; he rides like lightning." On another occasion, the same friend commented, "I rode over from Leipzig this morning paced by a fierce Yankee."

The tour included Cologne, Bonn and other cities along the Rhine. Sight-seeing was done in his usual energetic style. A side trip was made to Jena to see the glass works there, as glass blowing was of special interest to him in connection with his use of evacuated glass tubes in his electrical work.

Back at the university, he returned to his lodgings on October twenty-third to find a real surprise awaiting him. The entire Chamizer family was assembled in the hall to congratulate him on his birthday. A white cloth had been spread over the table and an array of presents set out, including books, a clay paper-weight, a leather case for postage stamps, an album for photographs, a huge plum cake and various other gifts.

The new academic year was just about to begin at the university when Professor Wiedemann suddenly decided that his health would not permit him to give his usual series of lectures on physics. His work had to be taken over by Drude, and the latter asked Will for help in the preparation of apparatus for the demonstrations. This new activity made considerable demands on his time, but he felt it would be good experience and might be helpful in getting a job later to have served as Drude's assistant. Moreover, this job relieved him of the expense of tuition and laboratory fees. He assured his family that, despite the extra work, his health was excellent.

The advent of winter brought discomfort. Leipzig's mud was worse than that of Boston, he thought. There was little snow, but a great deal of cold, rainy weather. "There's no more uncomfortable place on the face of the earth than is Germany in winter," he told his parents. "How would you like breakfasting every morning in a room with three great windows and no fire. You see, the Germans are too economical to keep a fire overnight and in the morning it takes about an hour to get any heat out of these ! ! ! ! porcelain German stoves."

Concern for what he should do after he received his degree from the university claimed some of his attention at this time. He was anxious to return to the United States, so he wrote to the Massachusetts Institute of Technology and made application for a teaching position there beginning the following fall.

By the end of the year, his little project was ready for publication in the *Annalen*. Including eleven photographic illustrations, it made fourteen printed pages.

One day that winter the celebrated Professor Roentgen came to the university. Professor Drude expected that the x-ray discoverer would make a visit to the physics laboratory but had to go home before the latter's arrival. When Roentgen finally came to the laboratory, Coolidge introduced himself as Drude's assistant and had a short talk with him. Having heard so much about Roentgen, Will was delighted to meet him. "I was very pleasantly disappointed in the man's looks," he said afterward. "He's not at all pleasant looking but appears smart." Roentgen's tall and powerful build also surprised him.

By the spring the main project was completed. It consisted of sixty-eight pages, each eight inches by thirteen inches and all in German. No sooner was it finished than he started to cram for his final examinations to be held at the beginning of July. He had been working terribly hard and had become somewhat nervous about the final outcome. "I bit off a good deal," he wrote, "when I tried to do two Arbeits, travel, hold down the position of an assistant, and get in shape for exams in two years. I think I am going to get out of it all right, but if I do, I shall thank my stars, and be a little more cautious next time. I think my nerve has often been better than my judgment."

But his worry was needless. "My trials are over," he said on July 14, "and I am Dr. Coolidge." Actually he received the highest mark in each of his examinations, and for his project. His degree was awarded with the coveted words "summa cum laude."

A few days later, Professor Drude presented Coolidge

with a photograph specially taken for the occasion and inscribed "presented to my talented and faithful pupil and assistant by P. Drude."

REFERENCES

Coolidge, William D., unpublished letters from Leipzig

5

New Environment

Coolidge's application for a teaching position at M.I.T., made while he was at the University of Leipzig, was received at an opportune moment. Professor Harrison Smith of the physics department had become ill, and a substitute was needed to take over his work when the fall term began. The job was offered to Coolidge, and the closing months of 1899 found him back in the familiar atmosphere of Boston Tech.

This assignment lasted for only one term. At its conclusion, he became assistant to Professor Arthur A. Noyes of the chemistry department. Noyes came from Newburyport, Massachusetts, and was keenly interested in poetry and sailing, as well as in chemistry. In summer he used to take groups of his students sailing while he discussed literature and other non-technical subjects with them. Coolidge regarded his work with Noyes as a temporary assignment for the remainder of the college year and he supposed that Noyes looked upon it in the same light.

This, however, was not the case. Coolidge remained

with Noyes for five years, working on a research project concerned with the electrical conductivity of aqueous solutions at high temperatures. Much effort was spent in developing a satisfactory conductivity cell, capable of withstanding the high steam pressures involved, and doing this without any leakage. To avoid any possibility of contamination, only platinum, gold and quartz-crystal were brought in contact with the solutions. He and Noyes published a joint paper on this subject in 1903. When Noyes became acting president, Coolidge took over some of his work in the physical chemistry laboratory.

Dr. Noyes' laboratory, where the research work was done, was in a room adjacent to that of Dr. Whitney. The latter was then dividing his time between the General Electric Company at Schenectady and M.I.T. at Boston. This kept Whitney and Coolidge in close touch, and the progress of the G.E. Research Laboratory was frequently discussed. Coolidge was greatly interested in this new industrial experiment, but always thought of it as something entirely apart from his own work. When Whitney suggested that he join the General Electric Research Laboratory, the invitation came as a complete surprise.

Whitney proposed that Coolidge make a trip to Schenectady to discuss the proposition. "I'll show you around and give you some fun and interest you like the devil," he promised. The trip was duly made, and Whitney was as good as his promise. On July 27, 1905, Coolidge wrote to his parents, "Have decided definitely that it's my duty to go to Schenectady—that it's my chance of a lifetime."

To permit arrangements to be made for continuation of the work he had been doing at M.I.T., he deferred his leaving for the new job until September tenth, taking the night train and presenting himself at the Research Laboratory the next morning.

The Research Laboratory of which Coolidge now became a part had very modest physical facilities. The personnel numbered about thirty. It was located in what was known as Building 6 of General Electric's Schenectady Works—a three-story brick structure built many years earlier to house some of the company's manufacturing activities which had eventually been moved elsewhere.

A machine shop and a glass-working shop were provided, as well as numerous individual workrooms for the scientists. Robert Palmer, a graduate of M.I.T. like Whitney and Coolidge, was responsible for the installation, operation and maintenance of all equipment. R. C. Robinson, another M.I.T. graduate, was in direct charge of the glass-working shop.

According to Coolidge's description of the building, "the workrooms were originally provided with doors, but these doors were finally removed because the director didn't like to open a door and disconcert the scientific occupant who happened to be busy at the time with his daily paper." It was, Coolidge says, rather to avoid embarrassment to the scientist than to increase output that this step was taken.

At first, the amount of physical equipment in the laboratory was comparatively small, but it grew steadily. The company was willing to secure anything for which the laboratory could show a real need. Coolidge had moved his conductivity apparatus to Schenectady, and this provided for him a useful supplement to the equipment already on hand. A few years later, when Coolidge was engaged in development work on tungsten, he was responsible for the laboratory's acquiring a wide variety of special, metal-working tools.

The personnel of the laboratory was growing slowly, although Whitney was having some problems in getting the men he wanted. Good research scientists were hard to come by. A majority of the best men were working in colleges and universities. They had the same misgivings that Whitney and Coolidge had felt about leaving their academic surroundings and plunging into industry. To meet this situation, Whitney enlisted the services of a number of foreign scientists who had received their training in Europe.

These men had been brought up in the tradition of doing individual work, and keeping both the nature of the work and its results a close secret from their fellow scientists. Teamwork was conspicuously lacking. A. G. Davis, the manager of the company's patent department, often referred to the Research Laboratory as the "menagerie," or the "bear pit."

This secretiveness was not at all to the liking of either Whitney or Coolidge. Secretiveness did not produce a congenial atmosphere, nor was it conducive to efficiency. To improve matters, Whitney established the practice of holding a weekly conference for the entire staff. A subject for discussion was selected in advance. Some member of the staff would then tell the group about his recent work, its problems and the extent of his success in solving them. At the conclusion of his talk, he would answer questions asked by other members of the staff. This did a great deal to break down barriers and foster a spirit of teamwork. Coolidge was a good listener at these meetings. He had a way of sitting back with his head a little on one side, paying close attention. Every once in a while he would nod just a little as though he had satisfied himself that he agreed. From time to time, he, himself, was the speaker. Commenting on this, Coolidge remarked:

"In Schenectady, I found to my pleased surprise, that Dr. Whitney had already successfully transplanted a lot of academic atmosphere from M.I.T. to the new laboratory. Then the strong effort which he made to have everyone in the laboratory know as much as possible about what every other member of the staff was doing, resulted in close scientific contacts within the group. Then there was the weekly, Saturday colloquium, which often brought a distinguished scientist from outside to talk to us. Besides this, we were encouraged to attend meetings of scientific societies, and finally, to publish all worthwhile results, and to do so under our own names, not just in the name of the laboratory. So, thanks to Dr. Whitney's influence, and the early success of the new laboratory, the misgivings I had had about the transfer, all proved to be unfounded."

In the same year that Coolidge came to Schenectady, the General Electric Company put its GEM (General Electric Metallized) lamp on the market. This required only 2½ watts of electric power per candlepower, as compared with 7 or 8 for Edison's first carbon-filament lamps. The GEM lamp was the outgrowth of an experiment by Whitney. He had developed an electric resistance furnace which could produce the extremely high temperature of 3500 degrees centigrade. It occurred to him that the annoying blackening of the ordinary carbon lamp bulb might be caused by the heat of operation driving off small impurities in the material of the filament. He wondered what would happen if the filament was first heated to a very high temperature to drive off impurities and then cooled before being installed in the lamp. He decided to try this in his electric furnace.

The effect produced was not what he had anticipated. The extreme heat changed the nature of the carbon of the filament, giving it a metallic character, and enabling it to be operated at a higher temperature, thus increasing lamp efficiency. This was recognized as the greatest single improvement in the carbon-filament lamp up to that time, and was in itself, complete justification of the establishment of the company's research facilities. GEM lamps were manufactured and successfully marketed by the company for the following twelve years.

Ways to improve lamp filaments had been under investigation in Europe as well as in the United States. Dr. Carl Von Welsbach, who had produced the Welsbach gas mantle, had invented the first electric lamp having a true metallic filament. This was made by mixing powdered osmium with a binder such as syrup of sugar, the resulting paste being squirted by pressure through a die. The thread thus produced was then heated to drive out the sugar, leaving a filament of pure osmium.

Welsbach applied for a United States patent for this process in 1898. His osmium lamp was about 75 percent more efficient than the carbon lamps then being manufactured, but it was costly to manufacture and extremely fragile. Moreover the supply of osmium was so limited that the metal from used lamps had to be saved and used again. Only a small number were sold commercially.

In 1902 Dr. Werner Von Bolton, a Russian chemist working for a German manufacturing firm, applied for a United States patent on a lamp having a tantalum filament. This was even more efficient than the osmium-filament lamp. It was reasonably sturdy and had good life when operated on direct current. Its chief shortcoming was that, when operated on alternating current, the metal soon crystallized and the filament did not last long. Since the generation, transmission and distribution of alternating current had been found to be much more satisfactory than the originally used direct current, and the electric power industry was rapidly changing over to alternating current nearly everywhere, the tantalum-filament lamp had limited usefulness. Nevertheless, General Electric procured an American license and manufactured a substantial number of them. One of Coolidge's first activities after he joined the laboratory was a study of tantalum.

A third development in Europe was a lamp using a filament of tungsten. In the late 1800's, a number of attempts had been made without success to utilize this metal for a lamp filament. In 1904, however, Alexander Just and Franz Hanaman, a couple of laboratory assistants to the professor of chemistry in the Technical High School in Vienna, applied for British and French patents on a tungsten-filament lamp. Their process of obtaining pure tungsten filaments was somewhat similar to that by which the osmium filament had been produced. Powdered tungsten was mixed with a binder to form a paste that was forced through a diamond die. Only diamond dies could be used in this process because the tungsten particles were so hard that a die of any other material would be quickly worn out. After the thin thread had been extruded, it was heated to drive off the binder. With further temperature increase the remaining tungsten was found to be sintered, or having its particles dovetailed together under attractive force.

At about this same time, Dr. Von Bolton, inventor of the tantalum lamp, developed a sintered tungsten-filament lamp. He applied for a United States patent in late 1904. Dr. Harry Kuzel, a German inventor, applied for a U.S. patent on a different method of producing a tungsten filament in January, 1905. A little later, Just and Hanaman filed their application.

All of these developments, were of course, known to the General Electric Company. They were, in fact, in large measure responsible for the company's giving Whit-

ney instructions to investigate the subject of lamp filaments and for Whitney's securing the services of Will
Coolidge.

In February of 1906, Coolidge switched from tantalum
to a study of the characteristics of tungsten. This was
basic research of the kind that appealed to him strongly.
At the same time it had a practical end in view. The more
that was known about tungsten, the greater the likelihood
of making effective use of it as a filament for electric
lamps. For a while he devoted part of his time to this investigation while he continued his study of the electrical
conductivity of aqueous solutions at high temperatures.
But he soon became so much interested in his tungsten
studies that he decided to drop the conductivity work.

"I am fortunate now," he told his parents, "in being on
the most important problem the lab has ever had. . . . If
we can get the metal tungsten in such shape that it can
be drawn into wire, it means millions of dollars to the
company. W and I both feel pretty sure of ultimate success and think that although other people are at work on
it, our chances for getting there first are good."

Leaving Coolidge in general charge of the Research
Laboratory, Dr. Whitney and John White Howell of the
Lamp Department went to Europe in the spring of 1906
to find out at first hand about the various tungsten lamps
developed there. They visited Berlin, Augsburg, Budapest
and Vienna. The lamps developed by Von Bolton, Kuzel
and Just and Hanaman all appeared to have possibilities,
but it was impossible for the G.E. men to tell from the

information available which of the three had the best method of making a tungsten lamp filament.

Coolidge, meanwhile, was working on a process of his own for making tungsten filaments. He incorporated tungsten powder in a temporary binder of cadmium amalgam which was then squirted through a diamond die into a bright, shiny wire. This was then heated by the passage of an electric current in a vacuum to distill out the mercury and cadmium and sinter the tungsten. By early in May, he was testing the first lamp using a filament made by this process. He felt sure it would prove better than any of the European processes. After he had gotten company officials interested in what he was doing, a most disconcerting event occurred. He found to his consternation that he could not duplicate the original mixture from which the filament had been made. Step by step he went over his process—and located the trouble. Cadmium amalgam had by mistake been placed in a bottle labeled Cadmium-Bismuth alloy. With this error corrected, he found the problem solved.

"This was a strenuous period in my existence," he says. He did not approve of Sunday work, but it was necessary at this time. The Lamp Department at Harrison, New Jersey was clamoring for material to make one hundred lamps immediately. By mid-June a sizable machine had been constructed for squirting the amalgam mixture through the die. "And that machine once running nicely, will produce enough wire to satisfy everybody," he asserted.

The Lamp Works was now getting quite enthusiastic over the tungsten filaments he was sending to them. "They are trying hard to get tests this week which will enable them to cable Whitney that our lamp is better than the German lamp," he told his parents in a letter. "I feel very sure that my contribution, the filament, is better and I believe that the lamp will be better, but they are trying to do a great deal in a very short time at the Lamp Works."

At the end of August, Coolidge received the first installment of Whitney's notes on the German process of making tungsten. It was not at all like his process, he found, and appeared to be much more complicated. He believed his process was far better and would be the one ultimately selected for commercial manufacture of lamps.

Coolidge had now become a big buyer of diamonds for the dies he used in his squirting machine. Often he bought as much as a thousand dollars' worth at one time as the breakage rate of the dies was extremely high. Most of the diamonds he kept at the laboratory but occasionally he had some in his room at home. One day a casual burglar broke in and ransacked the house where he was lodging. Fortunately, the door to Coolidge's room was locked and the burglar did not bother to force the lock. If he had he might have found several hundred dollars' worth of diamonds.

Whitney and Howell had ended their trip to Europe by purchasing American rights to the German method of making tungsten filaments. After Whitney's return to the laboratory, it was decided to experiment with the German process as a possible alternative to Coolidge's.

"It looks more and more as though my method would beat out the German method," he noted in December. "It will apparently be much cheaper."

"I am almost sorry that Whitney ever took hold of the German method in the laboratory, because he's having an awful time with it. But having started it, of course he's got to make a success of it. It distresses the heads of the company a bit, I think, to feel that they've paid good money for the German experience and still are not yet in a position to make lamps by that method. I think that confidence in the Coolidge filament is increasing daily. Already at Harrison they seem ready to believe that the filaments are O.K. and that their troubles have been in the *lamp-making*. At the present rate they'll soon be selling some lamps made from my filaments. And if they don't get busy at the lamp factory, Whitney is determined to make and sell lamps produced here right off."

For some time now the only thing that had worried Coolidge was the wearing out of the diamond dies on the very small filament sizes. But he made a big stride in solving this problem by simply turning the die around and squirting through it in the opposite direction from what was intended. He had reason now to feel *very* hopeful. Everything about the method seemed to get easier every day. Whitney said that he was sorely tempted to give up the German method entirely — but he thought that it would be wiser to keep on with it for a little longer.

Coolidge was working under great pressure at this time, often staying at the laboratory until late at night and coming in on Sundays, too. But there were occasional interludes. In February, the laboratory held a party. He told his parents, "All hands, factory girls (those making the tungsten filaments) included, were invited, and each was free to bring one friend along. There were perhaps 150 people in all. Whitney broke the ice by reading two original poems; and then followed a miscellaneous entertainment mainly musical. The feature of the evening was a little farce, a take-off on our weekly colloquium. Whitney came in for the heaviest roasting and I was a close second. The man representing me was named N-Thusiasm and he kept awake while the rest dozed. He also poured out the coffee from a big milk-can just as I have for several weeks, and sat with his hands clasped over his knee and his head cocked on one side and interrupted the speaker to ask questions just as I do. I had not expected to enjoy the evening but I really had a fine time."

In May a conference of company executives was held to consider what should be done about commercial production of tungsten lamps. Howell of the Lamp Department spoke up strongly in favor of the Coolidge process. He said he did not want to have anything to do with the other processes. Some of the executives, however, felt that the German process should at least be tried. Coolidge made no objection. He was confident that his process was the best, and was perfectly willing to see the other developed for purposes of comparison.

As matters turned out, little was actually done with the German methods. The Lamp Department was getting better results every day by the Coolidge process and began putting these lamps on the market. Called "Mazda" lamps from the name of the ancient Persian god of light, they quickly achieved great popularity. Nearly a half million were sold before the end of 1907.

REFERENCES

Coolidge, William D., "Autobiographical Notes," manuscript
————, digest of his laboratory notebooks
————, unpublished letters from Schenectady
Hammond, John Winthrop, *Men and Volts,* Lippincott, 1941
Hawkins, Laurence A., *Adventure into the Unknown,* William Morrow & Co., 1950
Howell, John W. and Schroeder, Henry, *History of the Incandescent Lamp,* The Maqua Co., 1927

6

Ductile Tungsten

The success of the lamp with the squirted tungsten filament left much to be desired, for the filament, at room temperature, was as brittle as glass. Lamps made from such filaments were very fragile and liable to filament breakage in shipment and in handling.

This brittleness seemed to be an inherent property of the element, tungsten. All previous experience pointed in this direction. The stakes were so great, however, that Coolidge could not bring himself to accept this conclusion without further experiments. Much effort had been spent on the chemical purification of the tungsten used, but, was it not still possible that the remaining trace of some foreign element might be responsible for the brittleness? To answer this question, he tried adding one foreign element after another to the tungsten powder on the chance of so finding one which would substantially increase brittleness and indicate that a trace of it might have been, in the past, the offender. In this series of experiments, however, the added foreign element invariably distilled out of the tungsten during the high-temperature sintering operation, and left no noticeable effect on brittleness. Coolidge therefore felt forced to conclude that tungsten which has been melted or strongly heated to its sintering temperature is, at room temperature, inherently brittle.

He felt that only one hopeful possibility remained. The high temperature used in sintering a filament had brought about a fully crystalline condition. Was it possible that the breaking up of the crystals through mechanical working, as by hammering or rolling, would do away with brittleness? What temperature would be required for the mechanical working? If the temperature were too low, the operation would certainly result in cracking and destroying the specimen. If, on the other hand, it had to be very high, it might be difficult to carry out, because of the limitations of the tools. To his pleased surprise, he found that good sound tungsten filaments made by his amalgam process, could be flattened out by pressing them between hot blocks of special steel or by passing them through a mill with heated steel rolls, and at a temperature of red heat or even lower. He found, furthermore, that the resulting flattened tungsten filaments had been somewhat strengthened by these operations, as a result of the local pressure and the flow of the metal—by the change from a fully *crystalline* to a somewhat *fibrous* condition.

These hot-pressing and hot-rolling experiments were later followed by hot drawing through diamond dies. This was accomplished by heating both the dies and the jaws of the pliers with which the wire was grasped. In this way, in the fall of 1908, pieces of pressed tungsten filament were successfully drawn through many dies, each a little smaller than the previous one.

The first tungsten filament to show that it could be permanently deformed at room temperature was a 9.8-mil amalgam-process filament which had been hot drawn through a series of five diamond dies. In this way, tungsten was made to lose its brittleness and even to become ductile when cold. It was capable of being drawn down to a wire of less than one-sixth the diameter of a human hair.

Lamps made from such drawn wire were so strong that they could be shipped and handled without danger of filament breakage. It is true that operation of the lamp caused recrystallization of the filament, with loss of fibrosity and, hence, of much strength. Even then, however, the filament was appreciably stronger than a squirted filament of the same size.

For the commercial production of filament wire, much larger ingots of pure sintered tungsten were needed. To develop them and the tools and the methods for hot working them, required about two years.

Coolidge tried at first to make large rods by the amalgam process, but, finding this difficult, changed to using no binder and subjecting dry tungsten powder to very high pressure in a steel mold. He found that in this way he could, by pressing from the side, make a rod ¼-inch square and 6 inches long, which was free from pressing faults if the mold had been made sufficiently rigid.

Such a rod was very weak until heated in a tube furnace through which hydrogen was flowing to cause partial sintering. It could then be handled and was clamped in an upright position in a treating chamber. This was a vertical metal cylinder also filled with flowing hydrogen. Heating current was supplied to the rod through the end clamps, and the temperature was gradually raised almost to the melting point of the tungsten. Occasionally air was drawn into the chamber, creating an explosive gas mixture which was ignited by the hot rod, and the metal cylinder was blown to the ceiling. Fortunately there were no fatalities. The difficulty was finally overcome by having the lower end of the bottle sealed by immersion in a dish of mercury.

He tried hot hammering such ingots, first by hand and then with a small power hammer. Some blows could be struck without cracking, but others not. A skilled blacksmith from the Works was even less successful than Coolidge had been, for the reason that his first blow chilled the work locally, and, from force of habit, he could not refrain from striking other blows in that same area, thus producing cracks.

Hot rolling was tried next, but without much success. Hammering looked better; but it was now clear that it must be under close control, both as to location of the blows struck and as to the amount of deformation produced by each blow.

This led to the use of the swaging machine, with a graduated series of steel dies. The customary long-bearing dies could not be used, but special ones with very short bearing were developed. The rod, heated in a hydrogen-tube furnace, was grasped at one end with a pair of pliers, and quickly pushed through more than half of its length into the swager, and then quickly withdrawn and returned to the furnace. The other end of the rod was treated in the same way. In this manner, $\frac{3}{8}$-inch square rods, after being swaged down to 53 mils, could be bent cold.

In the fall of 1909, Coolidge made a trip to Europe taking a few samples of the new drawn tungsten wire, to show to some of General Electric's foreign associates. This was his second trip in two years. He had gone abroad for a short time the preceding summer in search of information on squirted tungsten filament processes, and had made a stopover at Leipzig where he found all the Chamizers in good health and overjoyed to see him. In other respects, the 1908 trip had not been very satis-factory as the Germans had seemed quite reluctant to part with technical information.

On his second trip, he planned first to see Dr. Blau, director of the laboratory of the Algemeine Elektrizitats Gesellschaft, one of Europe's largest producers of squirted tungsten lamps and tell him something about ductile tungsten. He had a little difficulty in getting an appointment with Dr. Blau, but a meeting finally took place on November 8, Coolidge then showed him a small spool of fine tungsten wire.

"What is it"? Dr. Blau asked.

Coolidge told him it was tungsten wire.

"But," Dr. Blau repeated, "what *is* it?"

Coolidge explained again that it was tungsten wire.

Blau grabbed the spool and rushed from the room, presumably to test it. When he returned, he seemed almost crazy, so much so that Coolidge was worried lest he do harm to himself. His behavior left no doubt as to whether the Research Laboratory's ductile tungsten activity had successfully been kept secret from the entire European lamp industry, with which Dr. Blau was in close contact.

In the course of the development of the swaging process, some rods were made which were brittle even when hot. They were from fine-grained tungsten powder. On fracture, they showed a dark center, due to the incomplete removal of oxygen there. This was owing to the following facts: tungsten powder in contact with air, takes up some oxygen, and does not sinter readily until freed from it. Fine-grained metal powder sinters more readily than does that with larger grains. The outer layers of the fine-grained tungsten rods during heating in hydrogen, quickly lost their oxygen and then sintered, thus closing their pores before enough hydrogen could get to the central portions to free them of their oxygen. Drastic efforts by greatly prolonging the hydrogen treatment at lower and gradually increasing temperatures all resulted in mechanically unworkable rods.

In 1910, having satisfied himself that he must use tungsten powder of sufficient coarseness so that the rods would retain their porosity at temperatures permitting complete removal of oxygen throughout the rods, before appreciable sintering took place, Coolidge concentrated on the problem of consistently making sufficiently coarse tungsten powder. The method adopted consisted in the high-temperature firing of the tungstic acid, from which the tungsten was made, in a Hessian or Battersea crucible. Upon reduction, this oxide yielded sufficiently coarse tungsten powder.

As the rod increased in length in swaging, it became necessary to pass it through a furnace placed in front of the swager, and to use feed rolls at the rear of the swager. In this way, the diameter was reduced to the point where it could be hot drawn through diamond dies.

The wear of the diamond dies was at first great enough so that serious consideration was given to the practicability of hot rolling the swaged wire down to lamp-filament sizes. With a tiny mill having steel rolls only a half-inch in diameter, he succeeded, in 1910, in experimentally rolling tungsten wire down to 5.7 mils square. By this time, however, means had been found to reduce die wear sufficiently.

Before the adoption of the practice of firing tungstic acid in a Battersea crucible to get coarse tungsten powder, lamp filaments made from the drawn tungsten wire offset badly, and so had short life when operated on alternating current. This did not apply, however, when the Battersea crucible had been used. This had been predicted from microscopic examination of fractures of rods which had been swaged and then heated to a high temperature. Without Battersea firing, the facture would often show large crystals, while, with the Battersea, the fracture was relatively fine grained. Refractory oxides had been introduced by the crucible, from its hot walls, and these impurities carried over into the tungsten, where their presence interfered helpfully with crystal growth. Coolidge found that rare earth oxides, such as thoria, for example, added to tungsten powder in whose preparation no Battersea crucible had been used, also prevented offsetting, as did zirconia and ceria. This powder metallurgy had made possible the control of crystal growth that would not have been attained if the starting rod had been a melted ingot.

"In the mechanical working of tungsten, temperature plays a dominant role," Coolidge says in a paper prepared for the October 1963 meeting of the Society for the History of Technology. "Up to around 1500 degrees C, mechanical working tends to change the crystalline to a fibrous structure, thus imparting strength. Above this temperature, fibrous tungsten tends to revert to the crystalline condition. The best temperature for working, will then depend on the strength required in the finished product. If working is carried too far at low temperatures, the metal loses strength through the lateral separation of its fibers. The higher the temperature, the softer is the metal; and where much reduction of cross section is to be accomplished, it may be desirable to work first at a temperature higher than 1500 degrees, where the metal is relatively soft, and then to change to lower temperatures for fiber production and strength.

"The research and development work leading finally to the commercial production of ductile tungsten for various purposes was made possible through the close cooperation of many General Electric scientists and engineers— so many, in fact, that it would be impossible for me to name them all and properly assign credit. There was also help from others outside the Company. As an example of this, take the case of the diamond dies for filament squirting and tungsten wire drawing. It early became clear that we must, ourselves, learn to make diamond dies, shaped and mounted specifically for our tungsten work. Through the Waltham Watch Company, we learned of an expert lapidary, who came to us and stayed a month, teaching us something of the lapidary art. As another example in this same field, we learned from Mr. C. A. Cowles, of the Ansonia Brass and Copper Company, about their use of diamond dies in copper wire drawing. We were, at the time, eager to know what was the largest size of diamond die that we could afford to use in drawing tungsten, as this would determine the smallest size to which we must swage or roll. I remember Mr. Cowles showing me some very large diamond dies and offering to lend them to us, but that they looked to me too fragile and expensive for us to borrow them.

"Since adoption of the Laboratory ductile tungsten process, by the Company's Incandescent Lamp Division, some changes in the process have been made by the Division, but it is still one of the Company's most important applications of powder metallurgy.

"The successful outcome of our ductile tungsten work

was due to the production of the right microstructure. I must, however, say that we were guided, in the main, by the experiment itself rather than by metallurgical knowledge."

The making of tungsten lamp filaments by General Electric was changed over to the drawn wire process late in 1910. In the early part of 1911, the new lamps, known as Mazda C, were put on the market. More than half a million dollars' worth of pressed-filament apparatus had to be scrapped, as well as another half million dollars' worth of unsold pressed-filament lamps.

Because of the efficiency of the tungsten filament, the amount of electric current required to produce a given amount of illumination was greatly reduced. It is estimated that in 1914, the people of the United States achieved a saving of two billion dollars from what the same amount of illumination would have cost with the metallized carbon filament.

At first the sellers of electric power were much concerned lest there be a serious falling off in power demand. But it did not work out that way. In the first place, the new lamps could be, and were, used in many places where the older types were not used. In the second place, the low operating cost encouraged the public to use a great deal more illumination than ever before. As a result, the sellers of electric power actually increased their business.

During this period, Coolidge was appointed assistant director of the Research Laboratory. A little later, in 1914, he was awarded the Rumford Medal by the American Academy of Arts and Sciences, the medal being granted for "the most important discovery or useful improvement in heat or light." This was, perhaps, the highest recognition of the sort to which an American scientist could aspire.

REFERENCES

Coolidge, William D., "The Development of Ductile Tungsten," Paper for the October 1963 meeting of the Society for the History of Technology.

———"Ductile Tungsten," Transactions of the American Institute of Electrical Engineers, 1910

Hammond, John Winthrop, *Men and Volts,* Lippincott, 1941

Hawkins, Laurence A., *Adventure Into the Unknown,* William Morrow & Company, 1950

Howell, John W. and Schroeder, Henry, *History of the Incandescent Lamp,* The Maqua Co., 1927

7
Applications of Tungsten

The conquest of tungsten had been a long and arduous job. Coolidge compared it once to the practice of the locksmith's art.

"Imagine then," he said, "a man wishing to open a door locked with a combination lock and bolted on the inside. Assume that he does not know a single number of the combination and has not a chance to open the door until he finds the whole combination, and not a chance to do so even then unless the bolt on the inside is open. Also bear in mind that he cannot tell whether a single number of the combination is right until he knows the combination complete. When we started to make tungsten ductile, our situation was like that."

But, after the door had been unlocked, the way was open to progress in several directions. Coolidge had the priceless trait of inquisitiveness, and happily he received all possible encouragement to pursue his curiosity about other possible uses of tungsten.

The metal was bright and shiny like steel. It was immensely strong in tension as well as being extremely hard in compression. It offered greater resistance than copper to the passage of an electric current, but less than platinum. It did not tarnish upon standing in air, and was little affected by most acids.

These characteristics of tungsten suggested to Coolidge the possibility of using it for contacts instead of platinum in electric make-and-break devices such as relays and telegraph sending keys.

"This was not," says Coolidge, "in any sense an obvious application, because tungsten is not, like platinum, a metal difficult to oxidize. It might well have been assumed that under the heat of the minute arcs which form when the contacts are separated, the tungsten would oxidize at points where arcing has taken place, and that non-conducting layers would thus be formed which would produce a high and variable contact resistance."

This is exactly what did happen. Further study, however, showed that the trouble came mostly from the poor quality of the electrical joint between the tungsten and the contact-carrying members. No ordinary method would serve to solder the little disc of tungsten to the contact carrier. Eventually a solution of this problem was found in placing a thin layer of copper between the tungsten disc and the head of an iron tack. His laboratory notebook entry for December 28, 1911 says tersely, "For attachment of W punchings (discs) to iron tacks for contacts, get rid of loose particles of W on ground surface of disc by preliminary etching with fused KNO_2." Then the tungsten, the copper and the tack were heated together in a hydrogen furnace to melt the copper, which then formed a strong joint with good thermal and electrical conductivity. The shank of the tack was then pressed into or brazed to, or riveted to the contact-carrying member.

With the attainment of a good conducting joint, the situation changed completely. The contacts no longer rose to the same high temperature and the oxidation decreased to little or nothing. Thus, the use of tungsten contacts became entirely feasible.

Their great advantage was in their longer-wearing qualities as compared with platinum. The latter volatilizes at a much lower temperature and is thus eaten away. Besides this, the heat conductivity of tungsten is more than twice that of platinum, so that the contact faces do not rise to the same high temperature. Another consideration is the hardness of tungsten. It is so hard that it does not become battered down under the continual hammering that contacts get in service. Tungsten contacts show less tendency to stick than do platinum contacts, due to the higher melting point of tungsten. A minor, unexpected advantage was found to be that tungsten contacts are less sensitive to the accidental presence of a small amount of oil.

One day Coolidge took some tungsten contacts for automobile ignition to Dayton for examination by the well-known scientist of the automotive industry, Dr. Charles Kettering. "While I was there," Coolidge says, "he operated them on a bench setup and I was horrified when he picked up an oil can and approached the contacts with it. I knew, or thought I did, that oil would put electrical contacts out of business—they have to be kept clean. But the experiment proved very illuminating. Oil was bad for platinum contacts, but gave only a very temporary setback to the operation of tungsten contacts. They sputtered at first and then went on as smoothly as before."

Following Coolidge's experiments with the use of tungsten for electrical contact points, they were almost universally adopted in place of platinum or silver for automobile ignition systems.

While Coolidge was busy on the development of ductile tungsten for lamp filaments, a young scientist named Irving Langmuir had come to spend the summer of 1909 at the Research Laboratory. Langmuir was then on the faculty at Stevens Institute of Technology, but his teaching work took virtually all of his time and prevented him from engaging in research work which particularly appealed to him. He had done earlier work at the University of Gottingen on the behavior of gases at high temperatures, particularly in lamps, and had become intensely interested in the subject. At the Research Laboratory, he found two tools which he believed would be of great value in this kind of investigation. One was the G.E.'s equipment for producing a high vacuum, which was the best he had ever seen. The other was Coolidge's ductile tungsten.

"It seemed to me," Langmuir later explained, that

tungsten furnished a tool of particular value for the scientific study of phenomena in gases at high temperatures. From my work on lamps, I knew approximately the relationship between the resistance of tungsten wire and its temperatures and could thus use a tungsten wire as a kind of resistance thermometer."

The opportunity to devote his entire time to research, and the availability of these two excellent tools for the investigations in which he was particularly interested, prompted Langmuir to resign his position on the faculty of Stevens Institute and join the staff of the General Electric Research Laboratory. Thus began an association which was to have far-reaching results. Coolidge's work on tungsten was a great help to Langmuir. Later Langmuir's work on electron emission from hot tungsten filaments in high vacuum was to prove of great value to Coolidge.

In later life, Langmuir promulgated a theory in which he divided all occurrences in the universe into two types, one of which he called "divergent phenomena." A divergent phenomenon is what takes place when a small unpredictable happening sets in motion a chain of other events, thus exerting on the future a cumulative influence out of all proportion to its size. Certainly there never was a better example of a divergent phenomenon than the accident that Whitney's and Coolidge's workrooms were side by side at M.I.T., which resulted in the latter joining the Research Laboratory, where he developed ductile tungsten just prior to Langmuir's visit, which in turn resulted in Langmuir joining the laboratory.

The period following the development of ductile tungsten was a busy one for Coolidge. Along with the application of tungsten for electrical contact points, he was interested in a variety of other possible uses. His notebook records frequent trips to New York, Chicago, Cleveland, Toledo, Indianapolis, Boston, Washington and numerous other places. A never-ending stream of visitors came to the Research Laboratory to see him. He had been keenly interested in x-rays ever since his M.I.T. days when he had first heard of Roentgen's discovery. Now he began to think of the possibilities of using tungsten as a target material in x-ray tubes. Many of his visitors were distinguished physicians and surgeons who shared his hope of effecting improvements in x-ray equipment.

Another application of tungsten to which Coolidge gave attention was for rifle bullets instead of lead with a jacket of copper-nickel alloy. The principal advantage of lead over iron, which would be cheaper, is that it has a higher specific gravity. Because of this, a lead bullet will have a smaller cross-section, and will, therefore, encounter less air resistance in its flight than will an iron bullet of the same weight, and will, therefore, give a flatter trajectory and a longer range. An iron bullet of the same diameter as the lead bullet, could, of course be given the same weight by increasing its length, but this would require giving it a higher rotational velocity to keep its axis tangential to its flight. To impart the added rotational velocity requires energy and leaves less for propulsion purposes. That is why the higher density of the lead bullet gives flatter trajectory and longer range.

The density of wrought tungsten, however, is 19.3 while that of lead is 11.5. Moreover the hardness and high tensile strength of wrought tungsten would give it high penetrating power. Its high melting point would prevent it from being harmfully upset at the base by the combined action of the high temperature and rapid impact resulting from the combustion of the powder charge. These characteristics of wrought tungsten suggested that the possibilities connected with its use for bullets should be carefully investigated. Considerable experimental work was done in the laboratory and experimental wrought tungsten bullets were made for the army, but apparently never got beyond the test stage.

No matter how many different things were going through his mind, Coolidge was never too busy to listen to the problems of others and give what help he could. This was well exemplified one day when Whitney was preparing a lecture to be given before a large scientific audience. He wanted to stage a demonstration to show that air becomes conducting when ionized. The setup had to be simple and capable of being seen clearly from the back of a good-sized auditorium. One of the assistants in the laboratory had been working on this project for a week without developing anything that served the purpose. Whitney mentioned this to Coolidge when they were having lunch together. Within an hour after lunch, Coolidge invited Whitney to his workroom. There three toy balloons were hanging up by long strings from a single support in such a way that they rested in contact with each other. A portable x-ray machine had been set up pointing in their direction. Coolidge electrified the balloons by rubbing them on his hair. The like electrical charges repelling each other, held the balloons about two feet apart. The instant that current was applied to the x-ray machine, however, the balloons dropped back into contact again. The x-rays had ionized the air around the balloons and made it conducting so that the electrical charges leaked off.

In 1914, the laboratory moved from the quarters it had occupied for twelve years in Building 6 to a new seven-story structure directly across the street known as Building 5. This was the first building constructed by the company specifically for laboratory work. It was shared by the Standardizing Laboratory, later known as the General Engineering Laboratory, and the Research Laboratory.

Unusual precautions were taken in the design of Building 5 to avoid disturbance to delicate measuring instruments. All the walls and floors were of massive construction. In certain rooms, the floors were supported on individual brick pillars, entirely separate from the rest of the building, and extending down to underground cushions to provide vibration-free platforms for the instruments. Pipe wells were provided through which steam, high and low pressure, compressed air, hot and cold water, and various gases were piped directly to the laboratory workrooms.

But it was not solely the physical facilities that ac-

counted for the laboratory's growing list of notable ac-
complishments. As Coolidge once expressed it, a laboratory is "a group of men working in a congenial atmosphere."
The laboratory had collected a group of brilliantly pro-
ductive minds such as few, if any, other industrial laboratories had been able to attract. A new man joining the
staff could not help feeling it a high privilege to become
associated with such men.

One of the reasons for its success was teamwork. There
was no secrecy and a minimum of professional jealousy.
When asked by a newspaper man how he had managed to
conquer tungsten, Coolidge replied:

"Don't put all the emphasis on me. In the first place,
whatever I may have done, I did with the assistance of a
staff of able workers, and secondly, we all had the advantages of facilities for exhaustive research provided by
a financially powerful and forward looking corporation."

In an article in the British publication, *Engineering,*
reporting a two-hour talk Coolidge had given in London
on the development and application of tungsten, the reporter noted that, "Of his own share of the work, Dr.
Coolidge did not speak at all. It was always 'we', never 'I'."

REFERENCES

Broderick, John T., *Forty Years With the General Electric,* Fort
    Orange Press, 1929
_____*Willis Rodney Whitney,* Fort Orange Press 1945

Coolidge, William D., digest of his laboratory notebooks
———"Formative Years of the Laboratory," Research Laboratory Colloquium Paper, December 12, 1951
———"Metallic Tungsten and Some of Its Applications," Transactions of the American Institute of Electrical Engineers, 1912

Engineering, "Coolidge and the X-ray Bulbs," July 23, 1920

Rosenfeld, Albert, "The Quintessence of Irving Langmuir," *The Collected Works of Irving Langmuir,* C. Guy Suits, general editor, Vol. 12, Pergamon Press, 1960

8

Early X-ray Work

Roentgen first disclosed his discovery of x-rays in a paper presented to the Physical Medical Society of Wurzburg late in 1895. It was published almost immediately and created a world-wide sensation. Many medical men saw at once how the sufferings of mankind might be lessened by the use of the new rays. But there was also a good deal of misconception of what x-rays would do. Their ability to "see" through opaque material alarmed some people.

A member of the New Jersey Assembly introduced a bill to prohibit the use of x-rays in opera glasses at theaters. A London firm advertised x-ray-proof clothing for women. One New York newspaper reported that x-rays were used at the College of Physicians and Surgeons to impose anatomic diagrams directly on the minds of students in preference to conventional methods of teaching. Even the learned *Scientific American* was skeptical, saying that "the process will probably prove to be of scientific rather than practical interest."

Announcement of Roentgen's great discovery came during Will Coolidge's senior year as an electrical engineering student at M.I.T. It was soon followed by intensive work on the part of members of the teaching staff, on various forms of high-tension generators to operate the tube. This work was done in collaboration with Dr. Francis H. Williams of Boston, one of the earliest of the pioneers in the application of x-rays in the medical field, and it was Coolidge's good fortune to witness some of those developments.

In addition he spent some evenings with a friend who had a large static machine from which various x-ray tubes were operated, and he later built a static machine of his own for the same purpose. He became acquainted very early with the destructive effect of x-rays upon living tissue. In fact, it was only a few months after the announcement of Roentgen's discovery that he required medical care for an x-ray burn covering most of the back of one hand.

When Coolidge left M.I.T. in 1905 and joined the staff of the General Electric Research Laboratory in Schenectady, he found there an urgent need for a vacuum furnace for melting refractory metals, including tungsten, which were being studied as possible substitutes for carbon in the filament of the incandescent lamp. His early experience with x-ray tubes naturally suggested that any material placed at the focus of the cathode rays in such a tube could be either melted or vaporized and because of the vacuum, without contamination from the atmosphere. So he returned to M.I.T. and for several weeks, with the help of a large Heinz induction coil and other equipment lent by the physics department, he worked on the development of x-ray tubes in which, for the first time perhaps, one wanted the target to melt.

In these experiments he did not get beyond the stage of using graphite targets, because a better type of furnace had then become available. This was perhaps fortunate for him since graphite, with its low atomic number, was a very inefficient source of x-rays, and the hazard of exposure was less than it would have been with more efficient target material. However he was using much energy in the tubes and did not have adequate means of x-ray protection. In fact, when Dr. Williams visited him to acquaint himself with the x-ray output of one of the tubes, he said upon leaving, that in all his experience he had never before been so much exposed to the rays.

When, after several years' work on tungsten, Coolidge had succeeded in making that originally brittle metal ductile and had learned how to make good lamp filaments from it, he began looking for other applications. One of the first of these was as a substitute for platinum in the target of the x-ray tube.

The general method of producing x-rays, which was unchanged from the time of Roentgen, was: in a vacuum, tiny particles of electricity—electrons—were brought by the use of a high-voltage cathode to enormous velocities, and were then suddenly stopped by collision with a solid body—the target—interposed in their path, producing rays which radiated in all directions from the spot where the collision took place.

Experiments were needed not only to determine design features, but also to learn the best metallurgical characteristics of the tungsten metal for the target face. To facilitate the experiments, the most powerful roentgen generator of that time, a 10-kilowatt Snook transformer machine, was acquired by the laboratory. As the purpose of the study was the development of as robust a target as possible, the experiments involved serious overloading of the tubes. This overloading emphasized weaknesses in this type of tube, which manifested themselves in the form of punctures in the glass envelopes and in cracks due to local overheating of the glass. These troubles were subsequently reduced by operating the tubes immersed in oil, but new limitations then presented themselves. With the heavier loads which could be used with oil immersion the aluminum cathodes melted. Then there was the ever-present difficulty of controlling the gas pressure in the tubes.

For the target face, sheet tungsten was required, and it was found that this could be produced by hot rolling the original rods or, better, those which had had a certain amount of hot swaging. From such sheets or strips the small discs required were produced by hot punching.

The next problem—and it caused a delay of many months—was to find a method for bringing a disc of tungsten into good heat-conducting relations with the large block of copper forming the balance of the target.

There was, at that time, no known means for soldering tungsten to copper or to anything else.

At last a way out of the difficulty was found. It developed that copper could be attached directly to tungsten in the following manner: the surface of the tungsten was first carefully freed from loose particles of the metal and from oxide. Melted copper which had been freed of its oxide by treatment with one of the boron compounds was then cast in a vacuum onto the tungsten. Under these conditions, the copper wetted the surface of the tungsten as water wets glass, and the result was a union of very high thermal conductivity between the two metals.

The tungsten disc for the target must not be too thin, as, otherwise, copper will melt back of the focal spot and will, by its expansion, cause a bulging out of the tungsten at this point. Upon cooling, the copper will contract, leaving a vacuous space immediately under the tungsten at the focal spot where contact has thus been lost. As copper conducts heat better than tungsten, it is, on the other hand, better to have the tungsten disc no thicker than is necessary to avoid the melting of the copper under the focal spot. A thickness of 0.1 inch was found very satisfactory. Such targets were manufactured and sold by the Research Laboratory to manufacturers of the gas tube for about three years.

To avoid the melting of the aluminum cathodes, Coolidge tried replacing one of them with tungsten. This resulted in a tube which was hopelessly unstable; "cranky" in the language of the time.

In another tube, the target and cathode were both made of massive tungsten and identical in form. This tube also was very unstable. The cathode showed essentially the same heating as the target, and the positive ions which bombarded it were about as sharply focused as were the electrons striking the target. It was at first impossible to operate it for more than an instant at a time as, with the application of high voltage, the gas pressure in the tube would immediately drop. It later developed, however, that if the gas pressure were then quickly increased by means of the regulator, the tube could again be operated for an instant, and that if this procedure were repeated several times in quick succession, the cathode would become very hot and, in this condition, the tube could be operated continuously. This seemed to bespeak interesting possibilities for a tube in which the cathode could readily be heated at will.

The idea of getting electrons from a hot body was not new. Edison had observed it in the incandescent lamp in the so-called Edison Effect, and O. W. Richardson had investigated the relation between electron emission and temperature. There was, however, much skepticism among physicists at the time, as to whether electron emission would continue in case the gas were completely removed from the hot body.

At just the time, however, when Coolidge had become conscious of the fact that most of the limitations of the original type of x-ray tube were due to the gas content, without which it could not operate, and was wishing for a stable source of electrons in a high vacuum, Dr. Irving Langmuir was studying electron emission from hot tungsten filaments and finding that even in the highest vacuum the emission was stable and reproducible and that it was even favored in amount by freeing the cathode filament of its original gas content.

Coolidge thought that this idea might be adapted to the x-ray tube. "I. L. tells me," he says in his notebook for December 12, 1912, "that in his study of the Edison Effect, current from hot cathode is greater with vacuum of .01 or .02 micron than at higher pressure (except in case of argon). I will try this at once in an x-ray tube in which I can heat the cathode."

This led to the construction of experimental high-vacuum tubes with a heated tungsten filament as the cathode and a tungsten disc as the anode. Until these tubes had been continuously pumped for many hours by an exhaust system which was good at the time, but which would now be considered very slow, they showed some of the green fluorescence of the glass which had always attended the operation of an x-ray tube; but as the electrodes became freed of gas this fluorescence became less and finally disappeared completely. The tube was then stable and controllable, and Coolidge was able to satisfy himself that its behavior was the same as it would have been even if it had had a perfect vacuum. The positive ions, essential to the operation of the earlier tubes, were no longer needed and the limitations, most of which were due to the presence of those positive ions, were gone with them.

Dr. Lewis Gregory Cole in New York was the first radiologist to have his office equipped with the new type of tube. To introduce it and its inventor to the medical profession, he gave a dinner in a New York hotel on December 27, 1913, to which he had invited many prominent radiologists. A powerful high-voltage generator had been installed in the dining room by Dr. Harry Waite, of the firm of Waite and Bartlett, and with it Coolidge demonstrated the new tube. With today's knowledge it seems surprising that the audience stayed through the demonstration. Up to that time the capacity of high-voltage x-ray generators had been considerably in excess of what the tubes could stand for any length of time, but with one of the new tubes having a sufficiently large focal spot this was no longer true. Coolidge opened the machine up wide and, with the limited amount of protection which the open lead-glass bowl of that time afforded, the audience must have received much more x-radiation than they were accustomed to.

In connection with the commercial exploitation of the new x-ray tube, it was deemed necessary to give it a distinctive name. Coolidge favored the name "G.E. Tube." But, Dr. Cole at his dinner party, entirely on his own initiative, had formally christened it the "Coolidge Tube." Newspaper publicity following the dinner, had broadcast this name.

Responsibility for a decision between the two names rested with G.E. Vice-President Jesse R. Lovejoy. On a visit to Florida at about this time, Lovejoy had occasion

Coolidge with early x-ray tube

to visit and talk with a local doctor. This chance encounter solved the problem. When he got back to Schenectady and Coolidge urged the adoption of the name "G.E. Tube," Lovejoy said "No. The doctor in Florida had never heard of the General Electric Company, but he knew about the 'Coolidge Tube.' So that is the company's name for it."

Drs. Cole and Eugene Caldwell of New York, James T. Case of Battle Creek, Walter Dodd of Boston, George E. Pfahler of Philadelphia, Preston M. Hickey of Detroit, and many other radiologists were very helpful in those early days in the efforts to adapt the new tube to the various medical applications.

The gas-filled x-ray tube (gas-tube) had not been easy to control and its successful use had called for both patience and experience. It was probably due to the idiosyncrasies of that type of tube that it was not uncommon to hear an expert radiologist say that once upon a time he had made a wonderful radiograph whose quality he had never again been able to equal. There had seemed to be some mystery connected with this—possibly some particular roentgen-ray spectrum was most desirable.

A factor which had contributed to the difficulty of clearing up the mystery was the runaway tendency of the discharge through the gas-tube. This had made it necessary that the high-voltage source employed should not have good regulation—that is, that for any given setting of the controls, its voltage should fall rapidly as the milliamperage drawn by the tube increased.

As a result, it had always been very difficult to know what voltage had been effective in producing a given radiograph. As ordinarily used, the parallel spark-gap indicated the voltage required to initiate the discharge, but this was usually quite different from, and appreciably higher than the voltage across the tube when it was later carrying current and so producing x-rays.

With the new stable tube, in which the starting and running voltages were the same, it was found desirable to use a high-voltage source which did not have a falling voltage characteristic, but instead had good regulation. It was then possible to know in advance what both the milliamperage and the voltage were going to be.

Another factor which must have played some role in creating the mystery was the size of focal spot. In a gas-tube this was not constant but could vary appreciably with the gas pressure even during a single exposure. Not only this, but as the pressure changed, the position of the focal spot could change also.

There was at the time but little knowledge concerning the matter of focal spot size. It was quite common for the manufacturer to receive an order for a tube with "pin-point focus." Such a tube, had it been delivered, would, of course, have been unsatisfactory because of the drastic energy limitation which this would have imposed to prevent overheating this tiny spot. This limited knowledge concerning the size of focal spot was such a handicap in the art, that, for some time after beginning the sale of the hot-cathode tube, the laboratory supplied for educational purposes, with each one a natural-size x-ray pinhole-camera picture of its focal spot.

With the hot-cathode tube, in which current and voltage were under independent and accurate control, and the focal spot was of known and unvarying size and fixed location, Coolidge was in a position to attempt the solution of the mystery concerning those occasional outstanding radiographs that could not be duplicated.

Coolidge often wanted to test the results on a human being. At first he used himself as the subject to be tested, but after a while his back hair began to fall out as a result of too much exposure to x-rays and he had to find a new subject. He did not wish anyone else to run the risk of an overdose of x-rays, so he persuaded a local physician to procure for him a leg from an embalmed body. With this, he completed his experiments. Then, wrapping the leg in some readily available varnished cambric, he took it to the company's incinerator for disposal.

The operator in charge removed the cover of the incinerator and Coolidge threw in the package, making no attempt at explanation, as the attendant did not understand much English. It seems that after he left, the operator raised the cover and, looking into the fiery furnace, saw the varnished cambric unwrap itself, revealing the seeming evidence of a ghastly crime. He telephoned the company police, and a little later Coolidge received a visit from a Work's detective, who was in a very serious mood. Coolidge explained and explained, but never felt quite sure that he had fully cleared himself of suspicion.

The conclusion drawn from these experiments was that there was no mystery—that, other things being equal, *contrast* in the radiograph was determined solely by the voltage used, and that *definition* was a function of the size and fixity of position of the focal spot. Coolidge concluded that, if he had his choice, he would not use the rather wide spectrum of radiation which an x-ray tube gives, but would take monochromatic radiation of a wavelength dependent on the thickness of the part to be radiographed: but that, not having this choice, he must be content with that mixture of rays coming from the tube when operated with the voltage which gave the desired contrast. Increasing the breadth of the spectrum used, by making a part of the exposure with low voltage and the rest with high, did not help.

Early in the course of the work it appeared that if cathode and target were brought very close together, or if there were a sharp point on the cathode, a high-voltage discharge could take place even from a cold cathode and in the highest attainable vacuum. In poorer vacua a similar effect had been observed and described by other scientists. Upon learning that electrons could be pulled out of a cold cathode even in the highest vacuum by means of a high potential gradient, the question arose as to whether a tube based upon this principle might not, because of the greater simplicity involved in the control equipment, be more attractive than a hot-cathode tube.

Extensive experiments which were made at the time, however, as well as subsequent experience, substantiated the conclusion then reached that such a discharge is not sufficiently stable. Nor did it offer the great flexibility of the hot-cathode tube permitting independent control of milliamperage and kilovoltage.

World War I brought new problems. For use near the front it was clearly desirable to have a simple self-contained and dependable x-ray generating outfit of adequate power and maximum portability. It seemed especially desirable to eliminate, if possible, the synchronous, motor-driven high-voltage rectifying switch which was in general use at the time. This switch prevented connection of tube and transformer during the half-cycles of the alternating current when the polarity of the transformer was wrong. Elimination was possible if a hot-cathode x-ray tube could be developed which could be depended upon to rectify its own current. To meet this requirement it was imperative that no part of the focal spot should ever reach the temperature at which appreciable thermionic emission would take place, as this would lead to electron bombardment of the cathode filament, raising its temperature and so causing runaway with consequent destruction of the tube.

One factor was very favorable—the amount of available energy was going to be definitely limited by the capacity of the gasoline-electric generator. The "universal" tube with its solid tungsten target would have been safe for occasional use, starting with a cold target, but not for the very frequent use which the war service required. These considerations led to the development of the "radiator" tube with its composite target, heavy copper stem and external radiator for rapid heat removal. The target itself was that which had been developed earlier for the gas-tube, but much experimentation was required before Coolidge was able to free the large mass of copper sufficiently from gas. For x-ray protection, a heavy two-piece lead-glass shield was developed to almost completely surround the tube. This tube and shield served for both the United States Army Portable and Bedside outfits.

Coolidge knew of no light-weight, gasoline-electric set suitable for the power supply of the portable outfit. It seemed possible that a motorcycle could to advantage be used as a highly portable power supply and belted to an electric generator at the point where x-rays were required. Through the courtesy of the Indian Motorcycle Company, he was provided with a motorcycle, and on it he took his first motorcycle ride. One experience was enough to satisfy him that this was not the way to treat the radiologist.

Through the application of tungsten contacts in the automobile ignition system, Coolidge had become acquainted with Charles F. Kettering then of the Delco Company, and this connection suggested the one-kilowatt house-lighting set of that company. This was a light-weight, 32-volt, gas-engine driven, direct-current generator. What was needed was an alternating-current generator, and for ready adaptation to a high-voltage transformer which was already in production by the Victor X-Ray Company, 115 volts was required. The

Delco Company obligingly made changes required in the generator; but the engine did not respond well to having the full x-ray load thrown suddenly upon it. So Coolidge asked for Dr. Kettering's personal assistance. The latter came to Schenectady and spent a week at the Research Laboratory in so modifying the engine that it would promptly accept the suddenly applied load.

Dr. John S. Shearer, then professor of physics at Cornell University, had assumed the responsibility for the design of the "Portable" table and he cooperated closely in harmonizing table and x-ray source.

Shipment of the tube caused much worry at first. Previous experience was all in favor of a light-weight, open-work crate permitting the handler to see the glass, and so making him constantly aware of its fragility. But army shipping instructions called for a solid crate spring-suspended from the corners of another solid crate, and General Electric was told that the tube so packed must stand dropping from a dray onto a stone pavement. It was found that the tubes crated this way would stand this treatment, but, in the first lot shipped abroad in this way, 40 percent were broken. The laboratory was then permitted to use its fragile open-work crates and, when shipped in this way to the war zone, only 1 percent were broken.

This new portable unit had many advantages over previous equipment for military use. The individual parts were comparatively simple, light in weight and easily transported. There was no heavy storage battery to need

ie medizinische Fakultät der Univerſität Zürich unter
dem Rektorate des Herrn Profeſſor Oskar Bürgi,
Doktors der Veterinärmedizin, und unter dem Dekanate
des Herrn Profeſſor Dr. med. Wilhelm Löffler verleiht
Herrn Dr. William D. Coolidge in Rocheſter N.Y. U.S.A.
in Anerkennung ſeiner hervorragenden Leiſtungen auf
dem Gebiete der angewandten Phyſik in der Medizin,
ganz beſonders auf dem Gebiete der Röntgentechnik,
ehrenhalber die Würde eines Doktors der Medizin.
Zum Zeugnis deſſen wird dieſe mit dem Univerſitäts-
und Fakultätsſiegel verſehene Urkunde ausgeſtellt.

Zürich / den 14. Juli 1937.

Der Rektor der Univerſität   Der Dekan der mediziniſchen Fakultät

O. Bürgi.   W. Löffler.

- - - -

TRANSLATION OF ZURICH DIPLOMA

The medical faculty of the University of Zurich under the
rectorship of Prof. Oscar Bürgi, Doctor of Veterinary
Medicine, and under the deanship of Prof. Wm. Löffler,
M. D., confer upon Dr. Wm. D. Coolidge of Rochester,
N. Y., U.S.A., in recognition of his distinguished achievements in the field of applied physics in medicine, especially in the field of X-Rays, the honorary degree of
Doctor of Medicine. In attestation of the same this diploma
is drawn up with the university and faculty seals.

Zurich, July 14th, 1937

The Rector of the University
          O. Bürgi   The Dean of the Medical Faculty
                                    W. Löffler

recharging. There were no moving parts other than those of the gasoline-electric generator. The tube could be operated for long periods without overheating.The generating set could be placed as far away as desired to keep noise out of the hospital.

"The Army Medical Corps," says Coolidge, "courageously adopted the new tube and generator, and this in spite of the fact that no other x-ray tube could be used with the set, and that there was no other source of supply for the tubes but the Research Laboratory of the General Electric Company. Our heavy responsibility in this matter worried me so much that I felt I should go to France to make sure that this radically new x-ray generator was performing satisfactorily at the front. But we were, instead, allowed to have our Mr. Darnell go as our representative in France for the remainder of the war."

In 1927, the gold medal of the American College of Radiology was presented to Dr. Coolidge "in recognition of his contribution to radiology and the science of medicine." Six other medals he received later also made specific mention of his x-ray developments. He was made an honorary member of the American Roentgen Ray Society, the American Radium Society, the Radiological Society of North America, the American College of Radiology, the Dental Society of the State of New York, the Pan American Medical Association, the Roentgen Society of England, the Société de Radiologie of France and the Nordisk Forening for Medicinisk Radiologi of Scandanavia.

In addition to being the recipient of these many honors, Dr. Coolidge also received one of the most jealously guarded degrees in the world. In 1937, the University of Zurich presented to him an honorary degree of Doctor of Medicine in acknowledgement of his outstanding achievements in the field of applied physics in medical science, particularly in the field of x-rays. Few other laymen have been so honored.

REFERENCES

Coolidge, William D., "Autobiographical Notes," manuscript
_____digest of his laboratory notebooks

_____"Experiences with the X-ray Tube," American Journal of Roentgenology and Radium Therapy, December, 1945

_____"Metallic Tungsten and Some of Its Applications," Transactions American Institute of Electrical Engineers, 1912

_____"X-ray Work at Schenectady," Journal of the Roentgen Society, January, 1921

_____"A New Radiator Type of Hot Cathode Roentgen-ray Tube," General Electric Review, Vol. 21, 1918

Hammond, John Winthrop, *Men and Volts,* Lippincott, 1941

Hawkins, Laurence A., *Adventure into the Unknown,* William Morrow & Co., 1950

The Science of Radiology, Otto Glasser, editor, Thomas Books, 1933

"The Story of X-Ray," General Electric Company, 1963

9

Underwater Sound

On a Sunday morning in the early part of 1917, Coolidge, Langmuir and Larry Hawkins, executive engineer of the laboratory, went out to Dr. Whitney's house for a quiet discussion of some of the problems arising from the war in Europe. Although the United States was not then an active participant, Germany's declaration of unrestricted submarine warfare had drawn this country close to the conflict, and the navy wanted advice on a variety of technical matters.

One of these was underwater sound detection. The German submarines were sinking Allied ships faster than they could be replaced and transportation of supplies across the Atlantic was seriously threatened. With depth bombs the British had found the secret of wrecking submarines if they could locate them. The problem was to locate them when they were submerged and could not be seen. Because sound will travel a considerable distance through water, it seemed that the noise of the submarine's engines might serve as a means of finding them. Both the

British and the French were using stethoscopic devices on their warships to try to pick up the underwater sounds of submerged submarines, but the range of these listening devices was too short to make them really effective.

Josephus Daniels, Secretary of the Navy, had summoned the Naval Consulting Board and asked their help in developing better underwater sound detection devices. Dr. Whitney was a member of this board; Thomas A. Edison was its chairman. A joint attack on the problem by the Research Laboratory and the Submarine Signal Company of Boston was planned. Later they were joined by the Western Electric Company, long-time makers of telephone equipment.

Construction of an experiment station at Nahant, Massachusetts, was at once undertaken by Submarine Signal. It was completed one day after the United States entered the war. Langmuir was to be head of G.E.'s work at Nahant. A second experiment station was started a little later on the Mohawk River at Schenectady. Here Coolidge was to be in charge. Its nearness to the Research Laboratory was a great help in making quick tests, alterations and repairs. By a curious chance, the location of this second station was on a piece of land called "the Knolls" which later became part of the grounds of a greatly expanded General Electric Research Laboratory.

Just as this detection work was about to start, the famous English scientist, Sir Ernest Rutherford, visited the laboratory. He explained how the English were then using metal stethoscopes on their warships as receivers to detect underwater sounds. He gave Coolidge a detailed description of these instruments.

"Instead of starting with a faithful copy," Coolidge says, "I had an experimental stethoscope made up in such a way that all seemingly important design features could be readily changed while working with it, as, for example, the spacing between the movable diaphragm and the stationary back plate, the thickness and shape of the diaphragm, etc." This experimental stethoscope was connected by a short piece of thick-walled rubber tubing to a long brass pipe leading up out of the water, and through the usual stethoscopic connection, to the ears of the listener. The source of sound was a Ford automobile horn placed on a mounting in the Mohawk River.

"I listened from an anchored boat," he says, "and signalled to an assistant on shore who controlled and measured the current to the horn. The amount of current required to produce a sound which I could just barely hear, served as a rough measure of the sensitivity of the receiver."

Coolidge made one change after another in the design of the receiver without appreciably affecting its sensitivity. Even when the diaphragm was in direct contact with the back plate there was no noticeable difference. From this, Coolidge came to the conclusion that the rubber tube connecting the stethoscope to the brass pipe was actually the effective detecting element of the underwater ear rather than the metal stethoscope.

This was, of course, confirmed by removing the metal

stethoscope and closing the open end of the rubber tube. Such a rubber ear was not only much more sensitive than a metal stethoscope, but it gave a much more faithful reproduction of sound. The new development at Schenectady was passed along to Langmuir at Nahant so that experiments could be conducted on a larger scale than was possible in the Mohawk River.

The latter found that by using two such tubes closed at one end and with one connected to each ear, a surprisingly accurate determination could be made of the direction from which the sound was coming. This, of course, was based on the ability of the human hearing system to measure the difference in time between the detection of sound in one ear and that in the other, and instinctively to interpret this in terms of direction.

In connection with his sound-detection experiments, Coolidge wanted to know at one time how effectively sound could be transmitted through the wooden hull of a vessel. After some searching, he found a disused old wooden scow that he thought would serve his purpose. He filled the hull half full of water, into which he lowered the sound receiver. Then he seated himself in a chair on the deck and put on the earphones to see how well he could hear the signals from the Ford horn in the river.

A few moments later he glanced up and saw his assistant waving frantically. Coolidge looked around for the reason, and to his great surprise discovered that the old scow was sinking rapidly under his feet. Fortunately, a rowboat had been moored to the scow, and he quickly climbed into it, only seconds before the scow sank sedately to the bottom of the river. "This episode," Coolidge says, "somewhat unsettled my belief that wood will float."

The sound-detection work in the Mohawk River continued into the late fall. Manipulation of the listening gear brought Coolidge's hands into frequent contact with the water, which got colder and colder as the season advanced. He began to fear that freezing weather might suddenly put a stop to the whole project. When he conveyed his worries to Dr. Whitney and suggested that plans be made so that the work could continue during the winter, the director of the laboratory rather made light of the danger of interruption.

That very night the river froze over and stayed frozen over until the following spring. Arrangements were then quickly made to transfer the sound-detection work to the U.S. Naval Station at Key West, Florida. There Coolidge and his assistants were provided with a laboratory and a boat large enough so that the experiments could not only be continued, but also extended out into deep water.

It became necessary during the course of the work at Key West for Dr. Coolidge to take a piece of his experimental apparatus to Langmuir at Nahant. Shortly after he and Mrs. Coolidge, who was with him at Key West, boarded the train for the north, the doctor was approached by a local law-enforcement officer, who inquired about his identity and the purpose of his trip. The officer displayed a good deal of suspicion and took Coolidge to the end of the car for questioning. This created a really em-

barassing situation as Coolidge could not, for security
reasons, show him either the apparatus he was carrying
or the notebook which described its purpose. For a few
minutes, it appeared that the Coolidges' journey would be
interrupted before they left Florida. But, as the train was
nearing Jacksonville, it stopped unexpectedly on the
bridge over the St. John River. Here other officers boarded
the train and arrested a man sitting in the seat next ahead
to the Coolidges. He was an enemy spy who had slipped
over to the United States from Cuba and was making his
way north.

The twin discoveries of Coolidge and Langmuir resulted in the development of the so-called "C-tube" for
submarine detection. Under favorable conditions, it could
detect and locate a submerged submarine at a distance of
about two miles. Later came the "K-tube" with about five
times the range, but somewhat less directional accuracy.

To test these "K" tubes a detector was placed offshore
at Nahant connected to the station on land where an
observer would sit every night and plot the courses of
unseen ships entering and leaving Boston Harbor. In this
way navy men, assigned for the purpose, acquired skill in
the use of the tubes which were being installed on American naval ships being fitted for service in European
waters. To assist the students in this sound-detection
school, the aid of the Victor Talking Machine Company
was obtained for making records of various kinds of ships,
including submarines at different speeds on the surface
and submerged, and even the noise of a torpedo.

In November, 1917, three complete sets of "C" and "K" tubes were placed on board the battleship U.S.S. *Delaware* by a couple of engineers of the Nahant group and taken to England for installation on British ships for demonstration purposes. Through the good offices of Admiral Sims the approval of the British Admiralty was obtained and both "C" and "K" tubes were installed on three British trawlers. A demonstration was made in the English Channel during the last week of December, 1917, and the first week in January, 1918. Early in January, a German submarine was heard and after some six hours was sunk. This was later proved by divers. So successful was the demonstration that the British Admiralty decided to adopt this equipment exclusively as soon as possible.

It was the United States submarine chasers with their "C" and "K" tubes that cleared the Mediterranean of subs in 1918. That spring, and summer, Austrian submarines operating from Pola, at the head of the Adriatic were making the Mediterranean the most dangerous area in the world for Allied shipping. The American subchasers, by their continuous attacks with depth bombs on submerged subs, shut off the only passage to the Mediterranean and sank many submarines that tried to pass through. The curve of sinkings of merchant ships dropped from a high point in early spring to nearly zero before the fall was over.

Conditions for listening in the Adriatic were ideal, both because of the relative absence of shipping, which interfered very much in other waters, and of the great depth of water, which made the "K" tubes most effective even in bad weather.

The outstanding feature of the "C" and "K" tubes was their sense of direction and their accuracy, 4 to 5 degrees on the "C" tube at one to two miles distance, and 10 to 12 degrees on the "K" tube at from eight to ten miles. They were also sturdy, reliable, and thoroughly practical to use.

Both tubes were the object of a great deal of interest and praise by all the Allied naval specialists who had to do with the anti-sub warfare in Europe, and it was the universal opinion that these two devices were far superior to anything else that any country had been able to put into service up to the time the armistice was signed.

In all the war developments, in which, of course, speed was of the utmost importance, the scientists of the Research Laboratory had an enormous advantage, which was well expressed by a member of a British Naval Commission which visited Nahant and Schenectady in the fall of 1917. He had been amazed not only by the successful results obtained with the "C" tube but also by the fact that it was already in quantity production. He said that more had been accomplished in sub detection here in six months than in three years in England, and that he believed the reason to be that the scientists of the General Electric laboratory had right at their side a large and efficient engineering and manufacturing organization with which they had learned, through years of experience, to work effectively as a team.

Forty-six years after the initial success of the "C" tube, General Electric and the navy were still actively engaged in the development of underwater sound-detection equipment. In 1963, a former navy LCT was converted into one of the country's most complete sonar (sound navigation and ranging) test vessels and named the *William D. Coolidge* in recognition of the developer of the tube which became the primary submarine-detection equipment of World War 1. Moored in deep water in Lake Cayuga, about five miles north of the Ithaca laboratory of G.E.'s Heavy Military Electronics Department, this research vessel is provided with high-power linear transmitters, automatic plotting equipment and over-the-side booms for holding calibration hydrophones. Dimensions of the *RV Coolidge* are such, however, that it can move into other waters through the New York State Barge Canal and take position wherever it can contribute most to the never-ending investigation and testing of equipment for national defense.

REFERENCES

Coolidge, William D., "Autobiographical Notes," manuscript

Hawkins, Laurence A., *Adventure into the Unknown,* William Morrow & Co., 1950
———unpublished historical manuscript

Rosenfeld, Albert, "The Quintessence of Irving Langmuir," *The Collected Papers of Irving Langmuir,* C. Guy Suits, general editor, Vol. 12 Pergamon Press, 1962

10

Higher Voltage X-rays

Notable advances in the design of x-ray equipment were made in the years following the conclusion of World War 1. Science had early learned that x-rays are like ordinary light, only of much shorter wavelength. That of ordinary light is a fiftieth of the thickness of a sheet of tissue paper, while that of x-rays is about one ten-thousandth that of ordinary light. It was known also that the higher the voltage, the shorter the wavelength, and the more penetrating the rays.

X-ray equipment built before the development of the Coolidge tube operated at 30,000 to 40,000 volts. The first commercial Coolidge hot-cathode, high-vacuum tube was designed for operation at voltages up to 140,000 volts. Nevertheless, medical radiologists were asking for higher voltage—for radiations of such high-penetrating power as to make it possible to deliver a sufficient dose to deep-seated tissues without having so much energy absorbed in the overlying superficial tissues. High penetrating power is advantageous not only in itself, but also

110

because the scattering of the radiation that takes place within the tissues gets to be more and more in the forward direction. For this reason, advances in x-ray equipment have most frequently been associated with increases in operating voltages.

The first of the notable post-war advances did not, however, involve higher voltage. It was the Coolidge oil-immersed, shock-proof 56,000-volt dental unit announced by the General Electric Company in 1919. This was an outgrowth of the Army Portable unit, made possible by the fact that the tube could be made very small and immersed in oil, as it had a long life and did not need to be seen during operation. Because of these characteristics, it could be installed in the same grounded metal container as its transformer. Thus the operator was securely protected against stray x-rays, as well as against electric shock. Dentists had long felt the need for something that would permit them to examine more than the visible surfaces of the teeth and the superficial tissues of the mouth. The new, compact, x-ray unit was admirable for this purpose and was soon in great demand.

Up to this time all of G.E.'s x-ray equipment had been manufactured in the Research Laboratory. But the scope of these operations had now become so large that it seemed desirable to transfer x-ray manufacturing elsewhere and permit the laboratory to concentrate on its primary function—fundamental research. The company, therefore, bought an interest in the Victor Electric Company of Chicago, which had begun commercial manufacture of x-ray equipment as early as 1896. The latter was renamed the Victor X-ray Corporation and became the sole distributor of Coolidge tubes. A little later the manufacture of x-ray equipment was transferred from Schenectady to Victor which, in 1930, became the General Electric X-ray Corporation, and later the X-ray Department of the General Electric Company. In 1946-7, the x-ray operation was moved from Chicago to Milwaukee.

Even while the dental unit was being perfected, Coolidge was experimenting with higher voltages and by 1921 had developed a 200,000-volt unit. This appeared to be about the limit which could be obtained with the type of tube he was using. So he developed a tube of radically different design. It operated on what is known as the cascade principle. Electrons coming from the cathode pass through a succession of electrostatic fields before striking the target. Each of these fields applies additional velocity to the electrons so that they eventually strike the target at far higher velocity than could be imparted by a single field. This multisection tube was made possible by the development of Fernico, an alloy of iron, nickel and cobalt, having over a wide temperature range the same expansion as glass, thus permitting the necessary large glass-to-metal seals. The first tube constructed on this principle operated at 300,000 volts. Before long, even higher voltages were attained.

Speaking before the American Institute of Electrical Engineers a few years later, Coolidge said:

"This multisectional system promises to let us build vacuum discharge tubes for as high voltages as we can produce. This opens a vista of alluring scientific possibilities. It had tantalized us for years to think that we couldn't produce in the laboratory just as high-speed electrons as the highest velocity beta rays of radium and just as penetrating radiations as the shortest wavelength gamma rays from radium.

"According to Sir Ernest Rutherford we need only a little more than twice the voltage which we have already employed to produce x-rays as penetrating as the most penetrating gamma rays from radium, and 3,000,000 volts to produce as high-speed beta rays.

"What shall we do with the high-speed particles obtainable from tubes operating at a potential difference of millions of volts? The lure, of course, lies in the fact that we can't answer the question beyond saying that we shall experiment with them. They should eventually help us to further knowledge of the atomic nucleus and to further knowledge of radiation laws. It is, furthermore, not unlikely that therapeutic, chemical, bactericidal, or other practical uses will develop."

In radiography, speed and sharpness of definition are both desirable, but mutually opposed to one another, as the former calls for a large focal spot, while the latter calls for a small one. Only a small fraction of the energy of the electron beam emanating from the cathode—less than 1% ordinarily—is converted into x-rays, while the rest is delivered as heat to the focal area.

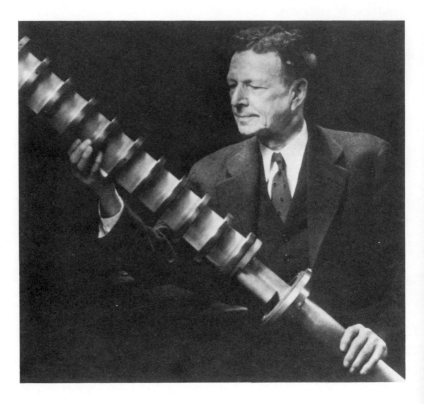

Coolidge with million-volt x-ray tube

The heating situation has been greatly helped by the development of the rotating-target tube, in which the electron beam is focused on a constantly changing spot as the whole target revolves. This idea was originally suggested by Professor Elihu Thomson as early as 1897 and was the subject of careful study during the 1920's. It became a reality, however, only in the late 1930's.

By 1930 Coolidge had been able to push the voltage of his multisection tube up to 900,000. Later developments were to provide even higher voltages than that.

The world was not slow to recognize the value of Coolidge's x-ray contributions. Degrees, awards and honorary society membership were showered upon him. Viscount Halifax, British Ambassador to the United States, said in presenting the Duddell Medal to him:

"I am told that few if any living scientists could match the benefit which Dr. Coolidge has conferred upon medical science in making the x-ray tube the most important accessory of medical diagnosis."

Industrial use of x-rays got its start in the early 1920's when medical apparatus was adapted to inspect metal castings. This was done at the U.S. Government Arsenal at Watertown, Massachusetts. The equipment design was developed by Coolidge and Arsenal officials working in close collaboration. A powerful x-ray beam was directed through large castings and onto sheets of photographic film. After the film was developed, it was carefully inspected to detect minute cracks and blow holes in the metal.

This was the beginning of a new non-destructive method of testing metal castings and parts. Previously it had been the practice to take occasional samples, break them into fragments and subject the fragments to close scrutiny for possible defects. This, of course, was a rather wasteful and expensive method of inspection. With the introduction of x-ray inspection the need for it was completely eliminated. Within five years, aircraft parts were being inspected radiographically by the aluminum industry. Next to take advantage of the new method were the manufacturers of pressure vessels who used it to evaluate new welding techniques.

Eventually x-ray became a standard tool used in many kinds of manufacturing. One important manufacturer is said to have used sixteen different types of x-ray units during World War II to inspect parts for tanks, bombers, gun mounts, armor plate, aircraft engines, turbosuperchargers, truck and jeep engines, and gun directors.

Radio commentator Linton Wells on the Ford Summer Hour, once told how the Ford Rouge Plant was using x-ray equipment developed by Coolidge and how it could make a photograph in two minutes which took from four to twelve hours with earlier apparatus. Wells took up nearly the whole of the program discussing the work of Coolidge and Langmuir. Charles E. Wilson, president of G.E. wrote Coolidge a note saying that it sounded more like a General Electric radio program than a Ford program.

The range of x-ray testing has been extended in more recent years in two directions. One has been to develop x-ray tubes and generators in the million-volt range and beyond, to probe through thick sections of steel. At the same time, apparatus has been scaled down to portable sizes and weights for use on thinner sections of metal.

In the midst of this development work, Coolidge was notified that he had been awarded the Edison Medal of the American Institute of Electrical Engineers for 1926, "for origination of ductile tungsten and the improvement of the x-ray tube." Shortly before the presentation was to have been made in the early part of 1927, Judge Hugh M. Morris of the United States Circuit Court in Delaware invalidated Coolidge's patent on ductile tungsten, holding that his accomplishment, considered as a product, was a "discovery" of a property inherent in metallic tungsten, rather than an "invention" in the sense required in patent law. (Coolidge later received a patent for his process of producing ductile tungsten.) Upon learning of this ruling, Coolidge immediately wrote to the A.I.E.E. declining to accept the medal. "Judge Morris has just handed down a decision to the effect that my ductile tungsten patent is invalid. This decision, coming from a man of Judge Morris' standing, proves to me that the best of men could question my right to the Edison Medal. My appreciation of that great pioneer, Mr. Edison, in whose honor the medal was established, and my admiration for its former recipients are such that I would not for the world do anything that could in any way detract from the luster of that medal, which should stand for generations to come as one of the most coveted prizes for meritorious work in the electrical field."

*Edison Medal of the American Institute of Electrical
Engineers presented to Coolidge in 1928*

One year later, the A.I.E.E. awarded Coolidge the Edison Medal "for his contributions to incandescent electric lighting and the x-ray arts." Edison, himself, commented "Dr. Coolidge is a fine experimenter, he deserves the Edison Medal."

A later development in industrial radiography was an instrument in which x-rays are used as a thickness gage without the necessity of making mechanical contact with the work. This has been of great value in jobs such as the rolling of sheet steel where the sheet metal may be coming through the mill at the rate of 20 miles an hour and temperatures to 2,000 degrees Fahrenheit and where the thickness of the sheet must be kept within certain narrow limits.

Altogether, from their original medical uses, the field of application of x-rays has been extended in many other directions.

They may serve as a means of chemical analysis.

They are used to measure the distances between the atoms in a crystal and so determine crystaline structure.

They reveal hidden flaws in structural materials.

Through the measurement of the spacing of atoms they make it possible to show existing strains in structural materials—strains which, if not removed, might lead to structural failure.

The very low voltage x-rays are used in microradiography as a means of studying the composition of very thin metallic specimens and to reveal structure in delicate botanical and zoological tissue.

Lastly, and to the physicist most important, the x-rays have, perhaps more than any other single agent, advanced fundamental knowledge of the structure of matter.

"There is something slightly mad about the Research Laboratory at Schenectady," said a popular magazine in 1931. "At one end of the first floor corridor, William David Coolidge is experimenting to see what will happen when cathode rays animated by 900,000 volts are hurled against a diamond lent by Tiffany's. He may be determining their effect on spores of deadly bacteria, or, perhaps on a group of bewildered cockroaches about to perish in the interests of science . . . . . "

What was happening was actually somewhat as stated, but there was nothing mad about it. In an x-ray tube only a minute part of the energy possessed by the electrons when they leave the cathode ever reaches the object being x-rayed. Most of the remainder of the energy is wasted in heating the target. The question of what would happen if the target were removed and the electrons were allowed to pass out of the tube through a thin metal window, was of great interest to scientists. Except for certain minor losses, the electrons leaving the tube would have their full quota of energy, instead of the 1 percent obtainable from the ordinary x-ray tube.

In the middle 1920's Coolidge began experimenting with the production of high-voltage cathode rays outside of the generating tube. Earlier experiments by P. Lenard had succeeded in bringing out rather weak cathode rays with some low-voltage equipment. By using the experience gained in the development of the hot-cathode, high vacuum x-ray tube, Coolidge was able to develop tubes from which very high-energy electrons were brought out into the air. With these rays he began to produce chemical, physical and biological effects, some of which have developed far-reaching significance.

Many liquids and solids undergo marked chemical changes under the influence of the high-speed electrons. For example, castor oil changes rapidly to a solid material. Crystals of cane sugar turn white in color and, upon subsequent gentle heating, evolve considerable quantities of gas. An aqueous solution of cane sugar becomes acid to litmus upon being rayed.

The effect on organic tissues is very pronounced. When a portion of the leaf of the rubber plant is rayed with 1 milliampere for as long as 20 seconds, the rayed area becomes immediately covered with white latex, as though the cell walls had, in some way, been ruptured. An exposure of as little as 0.1 milliampere for 1 second produces a visible color change with subsequent drying out of the rayed area to a depth corresponding to the penetration of the rays.

The ear of a rabbit was rayed over a circular area 1 cm. in diameter with 0.1 milliampere of current for 0.1 second. Within a few days the rayed skin became deeply pigmented and the hair came out. It was not until seven weeks after the treatment that new hair appeared, snow white in color.

Fruit flies, upon being rayed for a small fraction of a

second with 1 milliampere, instantly showed almost complete collapse and in a few hours were dead.

Bacteria have been rayed and an exposure of 1/10 second has been found sufficient to kill even the highly resistant spores of b. subtilis.

Electron-beam radiation has been employed in several broad manufacturing areas. Production of modern packaging plastics by chemically processing such materials as polyethylene is one. In the process, a bombarding stream of electrons irradiate the plastic to physically rearrange its molecular structure by crosslinking its polymers.

This polymerization results in a brand new material with improved characteristics for packaging applications. The characteristics include an ability to shrink continuously and equally in all directions upon exposure to heat; high melting point; great resistance to chemical solvents and environmental stresses; and, in the case of food-packaging films, without any residual "plastic" taste or odor.

Electron-irradiated polyethylene tape, is manufactured as an insulation wrap for motor coils; communication, low-voltage power, and other kinds of cable; and various switchgear, capacitor, and transformer applications. Electron bombardment adds great mechanical and electrical strength to the otherwise good insulating properties of polyethylene in this type of production setup.

Molded plastic tubes that slip over and insulate wires, conduits, terminals, cable, connectors and even irregularly shaped electrical conductors are other examples of items currently being processed with electron chemistry. The irradiated tubing does not melt, run, harden, crack or blister.

The grafting of certain chemical materials onto others is another production use of radiation-initiated polymerization. In this way, for example, textiles are toughened with grafts of high-strength plastics. Or plastics of one molecular structure can be grafted to plastics of another.

How far science has come in the development of x-rays and cathode rays since Roentgen's original discovery in 1895 is pointed out by Coolidge in the foreword to a General Electric booklet, "The Story of X-Ray."

"Roentgen would certainly be astonished," he says, "could he read, in this little book, what has come from the Pandora's Box that he discovered. So much has already come out of it that one might easily think that it's now empty, but, unlike the Box of the legend, blessings don't just fly out of this one, but have to be diligently sought. Dedicated young pioneers of the future will surely find many more treasures there."

In the summer of 1963, shortly before Coolidge's ninetieth birthday, announcement was made of the award to him of the Roentgen Medal. This is bestowed annually by the Society of the Friends of the German Roentgen Museum on individuals of German and other nationalities who have helped in the advancement and the dissemination of Roentgen's discovery in both the scientific and practical aspects, or who have been of especial service to the German Roentgen Museum.

"I am particularly happy to receive this award," Coolidge said, "because Roentgen's discovery has been the underlying basis of so much of my work over a period of many years and also because I had the privilege of meeting him when I was a student at Leipzig."

REFERENCES

Coolidge, William D., Acceptance speech for Edison Medal, American Institute of Electrical Engineers, 1927

———"Contribution of Physics to Cancer Therapy," Address at Memorial Hospital, General Electric Review, July, 1939

———"High Voltage Cathode Rays Outside the Generating Tube," Science, November 13, 1925

———"The Production of High Voltage Cathode Rays Outside of the Generating Tube," Journal of Franklin Institute, Vol. 202, No. 6

Coolidge, William D. and C. N. Moore, "Some Experiments with High Voltage Cathode Rays Outside of the Generating Tube," General Electric Review

"The Story of X-Ray," General Electric Company, 1963

11

Away from Work

Coolidge came to Schenectady in 1905 as a bachelor in his early thirties. Almost immediately he became deeply immersed in his work at the G.E. Research Laboratory. But he did not, except during the most difficult period of the ductile tungsten development, allow his work to completely monopolize his time and thought. He has never been particularly enthusiastic about large social gatherings. On the other hand, he has always enjoyed the company of congenial individuals. Before he had been in Schenectady long he had made the acquaintance of a number of such individuals and began to have a very pleasant life quite independent of his work.

He spent his first night at the Edison Hotel on downtown State Street adjacent to the New York Central Railroad Station. This was considered to be the leading hotel in the city, but its accommodations left much to be desired. "This hotel, the best in town, is decidedly bad," he told his parents in a letter dated September 12, "infested with cockroaches and bedbugs."

Later that day, after a good bit of looking around, he decided to take a room at 69 Union Avenue, near the campus of Union College.

"It is located about one and a half miles from the laboratory," he said in a letter to his father and mother, "and is very pleasantly situated on high ground. It is up one flight and is a southeast corner room with three nice large windows. It has gas and electricity, and a large wardrobe. A nice bathroom is nearby on the same floor. It has steam heat and a hardwood floor. The wallpaper is in good taste. The house itself is very pretty and but two years old. It is occupied by a widow, her son and one or two daughters. My favorable impressions of the place are probably due to the fact that one of the daughters showed me the room. Her mother was away but will be back tomorrow. The price is $4.00. Most of the men here advise me against going out of town so far, but the high ground appeals to me so much that I think I shall try it for awhile. At this time of year the walk is a very pretty one, running as it does by the beautiful grounds of Union College. The walk would, of course, do me good twice a day."

Actually a trolley line passed the door of the house, and Will could take advantage of it in bad weather. Then, too, he commented, "the telephone is in very general use here. There is one in my new house, so I can telephone from there to the laboratory, or downtown to engage theater tickets etc., or out to Whitney's house."

His lodging house did not provide meals. Mrs. Button,

his landlady, occasionally sent up a plate of fruit, or invited him for a meal with her family, but for the most part, Will had his meals downtown. This arrangement was not very satisfactory. Restaurants which looked good on the outside, proved disappointing when he came to sample their food. Moreover, he did not much care for eating alone, although he realized that it had the advantage of allowing him to have his meals at whatever hours were most convenient. Sometimes he took a book with him to read during these solitary meals.

After he had become a little settled, he called at the house of a friend, John Bellamy Taylor, whom he had known at the Massachusetts Institute of Technology. "I had a nice meal and a pleasant chat afterward," he wrote. Several weeks later he commented "I was invited out to dinner today to Robinson's. He is one of the men in the laboratory and was a student of mine at the Institute. Mrs. R. is very pleasant and they have a very attractive home. We had a very nice turkey dinner. After a steady dose of restaurant life, it seems awfully good to go into a pleasant home."

He was a frequent caller, too, at Dr. Whitney's home in the little town of Alplaus, across the Mohawk River from Schenectady. "Mrs. Whitney has been very nice to me," he told his parents. "She is a mighty fine woman, so fine that I would be willing to take a second copy."

Lunch was the most social meal of the day for Will Coolidge. He and Whitney soon formed the habit of having lunch together at the Mohawk Club, an attractive gathering place for Schenectadians in the old historic district of the city and only a short walk from the General Electric Works. Business associates and visitors to the laboratory frequently joined them on these occasions.

The real solution of Will's eating problem was found when Will joined the Mohawk Club on Whitney's recommendation. "I have made up my mind after considerable deliberation that I can't afford not to join," he told his father and mother, "as it brings me in touch with those men here who can do the most for me, and as I have to do it if I am to continue lunching with Whitney. It will be great for me as I shall now be able to entertain just as though I had a house of my own. I like to practice reasonable economy, but, on the other hand, I don't want to lose, say a thousand dollars later for the sake of saving one hundred now." He also found it a quiet and restful place to have his own meals.

Not all of Will's new friends were General Electric people. Not long after his arrival in town, he met three schoolteachers, Dolly, Winifred and Ethel, who lived near him on Union Avenue. "I called on the school-marms yesterday," soon began to appear frequently in his letters to his parents.

Will had brought snowshoes with him to Schenectady, but snow was late in arriving that year. "Dolly will be greatly disappointed if we don't get some snow pretty soon," he wrote in late December. "I may try to do some skating. There is lots of it here on the (Erie) Canal. But I don't feel the need of exercise here a bit. You see I do a good deal of walking every day."

Thinking of his parents, he added, "I suppose Pa doesn't mind the absence of snow this winter. It makes it easier to do his chores and, I suppose, to trim trees, etc."

A week later he bought a pair of skates. "I'm like a kid, can't rest easy until I've tried them," he said, "I haven't skated in 15 years." The next evening he went to a nearby pond which was electrically lighted and found that he had not lost the knack of skating. So he immediately invited Dolly to go skating with him the next Sunday at Ballston Lake about eight miles north of Schenectady. They went out by trolley and the trip was a great success.

Dolly proved to be a fine skater. The lake was four miles long and they skated the length of it three times. Many of the other skaters were using sails. "These were new to me, but I've got to have one," he wrote. "You make up a sail of some thin sheeting and support it on a framework made of bamboo or light pine sticks. This sail you merely hold against your shoulder and the wind does the rest. They make terrific speed. In a good wind I understand they can make as much as a mile a minute. There were probably 15 or 20 of these sails on the pond and they looked awfully pretty. There was little wind, but still the people with sails went *much* faster than we could skate. I must begin now and do more of this sort of thing. Dolly is good company because she is always so pleased to join in any strenuous out of door program."

The next evening Will went to call on Ethel. She was a teacher of German, spoke the language well and was anxious to practice. Will thought the young lady was "pleasant to look upon." Also he was glad to brush up his conversational German, as a number of the laboratory workmen spoke German but no English. A week later he said he "talked German with the schoolteacher for six hours."

Early in February he had the task of giving a lecture at one of the local schools on the subject of "Heat." Though he knew the subject well enough and had arranged a number of interesting experiments to accompany his talk, he was rather nervous about the whole affair. Dolly had lunch with him to take his mind off the lecture. A crowd of about 300 was in attendance that night including all three schoolteachers. Will talked for an hour and a half, and at the end, the crowd clamored for more. Vice-President Rice of General Electric congratulated him. The janitor of the building was heard to comment, "that fellow knows his business." Ethel complimented him on his easy appearance on the stage and on the clarity of his presentation. He was so keyed up by the whole business that he could not relax when he got home, so at midnight he sat down to write a many-paged letter to his father and mother.

Despite the rugged winter weather, he continued his outdoor activities whenever he had the chance. "Don't know what I should do if it wasn't for Dolly," he wrote. "She's always ready to go off for a tramp with me. Yesterday, Saturday afternoon, it was terribly muddy. But I told her she could put on a sweater, old skirt, rubbers and gaiters, and we'd tramp out into the country. But she was game and we waded through mud, water and snow for about six miles, I should judge. It was certainly awful walking. I got both feet wet but it did me a lot of good, and Dolly seemed to enjoy it. We were half starved after the tramp and had a late supper downtown."

The next day he and Dolly went to Albany, of which he had previously seen very little despite its nearness to Schenectady. They looked around the city and then had dinner at the Hotel Ten Eyck. It rained the following weekend, so Will and Dolly took the electric interurban to Gloversville. They were much impressed by the cars operated on this line, which were larger and more luxurious than on the other interurban railways in the vicinity. "The track ran right beside the Mohawk all the way," Will commented, "and the hills on the other side of the river were pretty nice. The ice was out of the Mohawk only in spots and was well piled up in other places."

On March 5, he wrote to his parents. "Have just been over and spent the evening with Dolly. She plays the piano beautifully and the music rested me."

But Dolly was soon to have competition for Will's interest. In a restaurant one day he "espied a young lady sitting nearby who looked very much like Miss Barker, the violinist, a cousin of the Robinson girls. I didn't dare to trust my eyes until she saw me and smiled. She had just come to Schenectady to give lessons here four days in the week, spending the rest of her time in Troy. She has taken a room in a house only two removed from mine. She is a very pleasant girl, so I was as pleased to see her as she seemed to be to meet a friend in a strange town. I am to be invited up to her place as soon as she gets settled."

A month later he told his parents that "Kate (Barker) goes to lunch and dinner with me the four days in the week that she is in town."

All these pleasant activities were interrupted by the arrival of summer. The schoolteachers left Schenectady for their several homes, and Will's work on tungsten was accelerating to a feverish pace. This was a particularly strenuous time for him because Whitney had gone abroad leaving Coolidge more or less in charge of the Research Laboratory. "I shall have to ease up just as soon as I get things where I can," he wrote in late May. "I hate to work tomorrow, Sunday, but my kid sister Kate, and my other fair friends seem to be all out of town, so I don't suppose I can keep out of the laboratory."

About the middle of August, Ethel came back to Schenectady. She had as a visitor her former German teacher, Fraulein Kadelbach of Berlin. Will took them both to dinner at the Mohawk Club. Dolly and Kate came back to town a little later.

Will's second winter in Schenectady found him devoting almost all his time to tungsten development work at the laboratory, with comparatively little outside social activity. He continued to see the schoolteachers and Kate from time to time, but not so frequently as during the previous winter.

Early in November, he and Dolly went on a picnic

supper to nearby Platterkill. Everyone else in the party of eight poked fun at him because he was the only member of the group to carry an umbrella. But, before they got home, the rain came down in torrents. "I was the one to laugh then," he said.

In January, Coolidge and Whitney gave a dinner at the Mohawk Club followed by a small theater party for a young M.I.T. girl who had recently come to work for the General Electric Company in Schenectady. She was homesick and the two men felt they should do something to get her better acquainted around town. Mrs. Whitney was in Boston at the time and the scientists had to make all the arrangements themselves. "You'd laugh to hear us discussing social forms—we know as much about it as a couple of cats," he told his parents.

At the schoolteacher's home he met a trained nurse named Gertrude, whom he found quite attractive. Will and Gertrude went for a tramp and took supper at the Rensselaer in Troy. A girl whom Will had known some years earlier came to visit Kate, and he took them to dinner at the Mohawk Club.

But social activities were far in the back of his mind in those days. Almost all of his letters to his father and mother were devoted to discussion of his work.

"Have the work fever again good and hard. Things have been going too slow lately, but now they've got to move for a while."

"I am working very hard, but it certainly agrees with me."

"This week was a rather hard one, as far as work goes, until yesterday. And yesterday afternoon paid for it all. I got some wire out yesterday that was ideal."

"Have spent the whole day in the lab and it's now 10:30 pm, so won't try to write any more today."

A new note is sounded in his letters in the spring. On April 5 he wrote his parents: "Tomorrow I am to have a nice little outing in the country—going up to Granville, N. Y., to visit Ethel at her home, staying over until Sunday night. It sounds dangerous, but I decided to risk it. I think Ethel's stock really has been going up some lately. She's certainly a very attractive girl. I understand she has a very nice home. Have met her mother. Her father is a business man—president of the Granville Bank."

Ethel's stock continued "going up." In the fall of the year Mr. and Mrs. Daniel Woodard announced the engagement of their daughter Ethel Westcott Woodard to Dr. William David Coolidge. The following evening Ethel and Will went out to Alplaus for dinner with the Whitneys to receive their best wishes. The marriage took place a month later on December 30, 1908 at Granville.

After a short honeymoon at Atlantic City, Will and Ethel were back in Schenectady January 9. Marriage meant the end of Will's life in the house at 69 Union Avenue and the establishment of a real home of his own. He bought a two-and-a-half story white frame house at 36 Bedford Road, about a mile farther away from the center of the city, where he lived for the next twenty years.

The development of ductile tungsten was now approaching its successful conclusion and Coolidge was extremely busy. During the summer his father and mother came over from Hudson for a visit in Schenectady. In the fall Will and Ethel went on a two-month trip to Europe.

A significant event which took place the following summer is recorded briefly in Coolidge's notebook under date of July 18. The entry reads: "Out all day yesterday. Elizabeth came (born)." When the baby was a few months old, Will drove her and her mother to Granville in the new automobile which he had acquired, returning alone the next day. June 12 he spent at home "working on auto." A worker at the G.E. plant once remarked that "Coolidge would have been a great mechanic if he hadn't been spoiled by being a scientist." After Will's ministrations to the car had been completed, he drove to Granville and brought back Ethel and Elizabeth. In July his father and mother visited Schenectady to make the acquaintance of the new baby. He drove them around in the new auto to see the sights of the Mohawk Valley.

Coolidge was now busily engaged in the development of his improved type of x-ray tube. He was making good progress, but it was not all clear sailing. A notebook entry for May 8, 1912 reads "This is the crankiest tube I've ever seen." He was travelling a good deal to attend meetings of various scientific societies. When he was at the laboratory he had a steady stream of visitors, many of them being medical men interested in x-rays.

The following fall he made another trip abroad, sailing for Germany on October 25. Returning on the S.S.

George Washington, he reached New York on November 24. Ethel did not accompany him on this trip. Her absence is explained by his notebook entry for December 30, 1913 saying simply "Lawrence born."

A characteristic notebook entry for this period says: "Sewell Cabot here re his C.P. machine. Dr. Dodd here all AM. Prof. Abraham from Paris saw tube." This continued steadily through the year 1914.

Early in 1915 Ethel became seriously ill. To meet the emergency created by her illness and the presence of two small children in the house, Will was fortunately able to secure the assistance of Dorothy Elizabeth MacHaffie, a graduate nurse from Ellis Hospital in Schenectady. A native of Moncton, New Brunswick, she was an exceedingly calm and competent person as well as being skillful with children. When Ethel finally had to be hospitalized, she was not going to feel comfortable in leaving Elizabeth and baby Lawrence in the care of the maid and nursemaid, so she asked Dorothy if she would stay at the house and supervise the care of the children, especially the baby. At the hospital, despite everything that medical science could do for her, Ethel died on February 20.

After ten days, Will returned to his work at the laboratory while Dorothy MacHaffie remained at 36 Bedford Road to look after Elizabeth and young Lawrence. In this she was aided for some time by Will's mother and by frequent visits from Ethel's Aunt Carrie of Saratoga Springs.

As Coolidge had never concerned himself much with

the running of the household, this arrangement was a boon to him. Moreover, Dorothy was a restful and companionable person, having immense admiration for Will's work without really understanding its scientific aspects. A little more than a year after Ethel's death, Will and Dorothy were married.

Until he had established himself in his own house, Will had had limited opportunity to practice his favorite hobby —photography. This had its beginning many years earlier at Hudson with a homemade camera and makeshift darkroom. While attending the University of Leipzig he had continued to practice his hobby, taking many pictures in the city and on his travels in Germany and Italy. He had rigged up an improvised darkroom in the Chamizer house in Leipzig, where he developed and printed his pictures. As soon as possible after moving into 36 Bedford Road he provided himself with similar facilities.

With the appearance of the Eastman 16 millimeter movie camera, Will began taking moving pictures—first in black and white, and then in color. He finally concluded, however, that too many of his movies were of things that were not moving, so he bought a Leica camera for taking still pictures.

With the proper attachment, he was able to make stereo pictures and then to project them on a metal screen, from which they could be viewed through polaroid glasses. He was so impressed by some of these projected stereo slides that he used nothing but stereo on one Florida vacation trip. The result, however, was quite

Coolidge grandchildren looking at
enlarged photograph of grandfather

disappointing. "I think," he says, "because I was so familiar with the subjects that even when viewing the projected slides with only one eye, my mind supplied the third dimension, and stereo was not needed." This, plus the need of the special taking and projecting equipment, made him give up stereo.

Then, for making color prints, he was given a Lerochrome One-shot camera with which he could, upon pressing the button, simultaneously expose three films, each through its proper filter. For prints, he used the carbro process. The results were very pleasing but the operation of getting from the three negatives to a print was very time-consuming—about three and a half hours for each picture.

When the Eastman Company later brought out its dye-transfer process, Coolidge visited the research laboratory there where Dr. Mees put him for a day in the experienced hands of Mr. Condex, who had had much to do with the development of this process. With this start, he was able to get along quite successfully with dye-transfer, and found it much less time-consuming than the carbro process.

Since then, he has found, however, that, where only one print is wanted of a picture which isn't too complicated, it is simpler to make a black and white enlargement from a negative of a color slide and then hand-color this with transparent oil paints. This procedure also offers the advantage of more freedom (permitting changes in the color of costumes for example), and the opportunity, if desired, of adding white lead to transparent oil color (for opacity) and then painting out anything not wanted in the final picture. For color slides, he has for years used a Leica camera with 35, 50 and 85 millimeter lenses.

Commenting on his hobby he says,
"One of my most interesting experiences with the camera was in connection with a trip to Chichin Itza and Ushmal in Yucatan in 1949. Here we saw ruins of the old Mayan civilization—saw something of what this people, without metal tools, without beasts of burden and without the invention of the wheel, had accomplished in the building of wonderful stone temples and other structures and stone-paved roads.

"Imagine my delight when on the return trip home, in a book-store in New Orleans, I discovered and bought a two-volume work by John L. Stevens entitled "Incidents of Travel in Yucatan," published by Harper & Brothers in 1848. It was illustrated by 120 steel-engravings from Daguerreotype views and camera obscura drawings made by a Mr. Catherwood. It was quite thrilling to be able, when we got home, to compare our pictures with those made by Catherwood of the same structures a hundred years earlier. It also served to remove any doubts which one might otherwise have entertained, concerning the faithfulness of the restoration work which has been done since Stevens' visit."

When the Coolidges moved in 1927 from 36 Bedford Road to a larger house at 1480 Lenox Road, he equipped the basement with a studio for storing and displaying his slides as well as a small photographic darkroom. His collection of slides has grown steadily, covering a wide variety of subjects and places. Showing them to people who are interested has always been a pleasure to him.

This studio serves also as a book overflow from his study which is packed with books which he has collected over the years. These cover a wide variety of subjects which have interested him. Books on history and travel occupy a prominent place; few deal directly with the scientific aspects of his work. All bear indications of having been carefully read.

Another room in the basement has been fitted up as a machine shop. It is equipped with a good 8-inch lathe, a small milling machine, an upright drill, a band saw, a scroll saw, a grinder and many hand tools. Thus he is well equipped for working with wood, plexiglass or metal.

This has made it easy for him to construct simple gadgets connected with photography, as well as minor conveniences for the home."The main excuse for all this equipment," he says, "is that I enjoy using it and find such occupation very restful. Perhaps it does for me what knitting does for the ladies."

In 1947, shortly after his retirement from his job as director of the Research Laboratory, he was asked to spend several months at Richland, Washington, to establish a small branch of the Schenectady Research Laboratory to help on problems of plutonium production at the Hanford Works. One of the company's pleasant residences there was refurbished for occupancy by the Coolidges. When he arrived, he discovered to his great surprise that it had been equipped with a new and most modern photographic laboratory for his use. As a result, he was greatly aided in his photographic activities and secured many unusual pictures of the area and people connected with the Hanford Works.

REFERENCES

Coolidge, William D., unpublished letters to his parents
————unpublished notes on photography.

12

Head of the Laboratory

Willis Rodney Whitney retired as director of the Research Laboratory in the latter part of 1932. His strenuous activities had put considerable strain on his health, and he decided it was time to take things a little easier. To succeed him, William David Coolidge, who had been associate director since 1928, was named director.

It was a difficult time to take over the directorship. The business depression, which began in 1929, had hit the General Electric Company very hard by 1931. Many employees had had to be dropped from the payroll, and the work week of many others had been reduced. The Research Laboratory had not been immune to the effects of the curtailment. The year 1932 was not much of an improvement over the preceding year. Better times were on the way, but they had not yet arrived. The director was faced with many and complex problems.

Upon assuming the directorship of the laboratory, Coolidge made only one change in the accustomed routine; he took steps toward doing away with the practice of everyone punching a time clock.

Time clocks had been a tradition in the G.E. Schenectady Works since the company had first been established. When Whitney had organized a small research laboratory, he had asked for no exemptions from the regular procedure. But in 1932, the laboratory was no longer a small untried component of the company. It had become a large organization and had ceased to be an experiment. It could, to some extent, make its own rules. Coolidge thought that punching a time clock was wrong in principle for people doing creative work. What counted was output rather than hours spent in the laboratory.

"Punching the clock has become a habit with our people," he told company president Gerard Swope, "so that one feels virtuous in coming to the laboratory and punching, even on a morning when it would be much better for the company if he stayed in bed or did something else."

"But," said Mr. Swope, "you've always done it?"

"Yes," Coolidge replied, "that is true."

Mr. Swope was inclined to feel that the practice should be continued, but they compromised for the time being by taking a few names off the clock. A little later the new director took off a few more. Then another group was removed. He kept removing names until all the research personnel was off the clock.

"There was another important reason for taking this step," Coolidge says. "The industrial research laboratory, in seeking additions to its staff, is in competition with colleges, which can offer as an inducement, the prospect of 'academic freedom'. The time clock seemed to me the very antithesis of this. I have never been aware of anyone's taking unfair advantage of the freedom."

On November 23, 1932 a large banquet was held in Schenectady "to honor three of the city's most distinguished scientists"—Whitney, Coolidge and Langmuir. The last-mentioned had just received notification that he had been selected to receive the Nobel Prize in chemistry. President Frank P. Day of Union College conveyed the city's appreciation for what these three scientists had done in the past and its belief and confidence in them for the future. After lauding the work of Langmuir, Dr. Day continued, "Now it is always wise when praising a professor, to speak a few kind words to the president of the college . . . Dr. Coolidge came to the General Electric Company in 1905, whereas Dr. Langmuir arrived in 1909. It is difficult to get off the starting mark ahead of a New Englander named Coolidge. Like Langmuir, Coolidge is badly in need of a large fireproof vault in which to store his testimonials, medals and honorary degrees. He is known throughout the civilized world for his work on tungsten and for his contributions to radiology and medicine as the inventor of the Coolidge x-ray tube. He should not be confused with another great personage of the same name who has reinforced his fame through silence, and the cryptic remark, 'I do not choose to run'. For our Coolidge runs all the time, in fact he runs the General Electric Research Laboratory."

The following year witnessed an astonishing outgrowth

of one of Coolidge's ideas. He had arranged several years earlier for the Research Laboratory to construct, for the education of its own personnel, replicas of a few of the classical experiments in modern physics such as the oil-drop experiment by which Millikan measured the charge of an electron, the fog-chamber experiment by which Wilson made visible the paths of alpha and beta rays, and the experiment by which Barkhausen made audible the step-by-step nature of the process of magnetization.

These demonstrations had interested many of the visitors who came to the laboratory as well as its own personnel. So the laboratory supplemented them by constructing apparatus to illustrate a number of its own experiments and developments. Some of these were constructed in portable form so that they could be used in scientific lectures by members of the staff.

A much wider and keener popular interest was aroused than anyone had anticipated. Another series of demonstrations was, therefore, prepared for use before non-technical audiences. The Century of Progress, held in Chicago in 1933, seemed to offer an opportunity to bring these demonstrations before a very large audience, and the so-called "House of Magic," a name which made the laboratory scientists shudder, was made a prominent part of the General Electric exhibit at the Fair. Nearly a million and a half people attended these demonstrations. But the demand was still unsatisfied. The Franklin Institute asked to see them, and they were taken to Philadelphia for a week after the Century of Progress closed.

Later they were taken to New York. Requests continued to pour in and a second set of apparatus was built. Finally the "House of Magic" became a kind of road show which toured the country with a new set of demonstrations each year. A special unit was created to give shows abroad. As a combination of education and entertainment these shows had few rivals.

A notable event during 1933, which was an outgrowth of Coolidge's earlier work, was the installation of an 800,000-volt x-ray therapy unit at Mercy Hospital in Chicago. Most of the equipment was designed and built by the General Electric X-Ray Corporation, but the x-ray tube itself was developed at Schenectady in the Research Laboratory. It differed from previous tubes mainly in the construction of the target which was capable of continuously handling considerably more energy than had ever been handled before.

In the latter part of the year the Coolidges made an extended trip to England, France, Holland, Germany and Russia. Never having been there before, they found Russia particularly interesting. Will spent most of his time there visiting scientists in laboratories while Dorothy indulged in sightseeing and visits to museums and picture galleries. Everywhere they met with courteous and cordial treatment.

Russia at that time, Coolidge thought, was very backward in the technological arts, but was quite conscious of this situation, and was taking vigorous steps to rectify it. The researches that he saw in progress in the fields of

chemistry and physics impressed him greatly and con-
vinced him that the United States should keep in close
touch with Russian research efforts in these fields.

In Leningrad he visited the laboratory of the celebrated Dr. Ivan Pavlov who had previously visited the
G.E. Research Laboratory in Schenectady. There Will
met one of the famous dogs who for thirteen years had
been participating in the Pavlov "conditioned reflex"
experiments. This dog, Dr. Pavlov said could count up to
fifty and could distinguish between sounds of 500 and
502 vibrations per second. Will noted that the dog seemed
to enjoy the experiments, which brought to him a bit of
food after certain signals but not after others.

Both of the Coolidges were interested, not only in con-
temporary Russia, but also in the many evidences of her
past greatness as indicated by the handsome palaces,
museums, theaters, etc. This impression was strengthened
by an elaborate state dinner of traditional type in honor
of Colonel and Mrs. Charles Lindbergh and Senator and
Mrs. Reynolds of North Carolina, to which the Coolidges
were invited. Colonel Lindbergh later called upon Will
and Dorothy at their hotel.

The combination of work and official functions made
this a strenuous period. Dorothy wrote to Lawrence
Coolidge back in the United States "Dad is working terribly hard. I don't see how he keeps up the pace. He
looks well, tho."

Responsibility for the x-ray work of the Research Laboratory was given to Dr. E. E. Charlton when Coolidge

became director. He was assisted by W. F. Westendorp and others. A low-frequency, resonance transformer developed by Westendorp was an important contribution to the advancement of x-ray technology. This required no iron in the center, thus permitting the x-ray tube to be placed there, where it would be electrostatically shielded by the transformer, and where the connections between tube and transformer would be very short and also completely shielded.

The goal which the laboratory had set was the development of an x-ray unit capable of operation at more than a million volts and still of so small a size that it could be installed in existing hospital rooms. This called for an insulating medium having a much higher dielectric strength than the transformer oil which had been used in the past. The laboratory became interested in various other liquids and gases. It was found that a certain experimental transformer would arc over at 150,000 volts when air at atmospheric pressure was used as a dielectric. The same transformer, when filled with oil, would arc over at about 600,000 volts. When filled with one of the Freon gases used in refrigeration, at a pressure of 70 pounds per square inch, it would arc over at about 1,500,-000 volts. In other words, the compressed Freon gas had ten times the dielectric strength of free air and two and a half times that of transformer oil.

By 1939 a million-volt x-ray unit had been developed incorporating the basic principles of the multi-section tube, the resonant transformer and gas insulation. Four years later a two-million-volt unit was announced. It would have been possible to build x-ray generators for still higher voltages by this method, but not without undesirable increase in size.

In an ordinary step-up transformer the changing current in the primary winding produces a changing magnetic field which, in turn, induces a changing electric field in the secondary winding with its many turns, thus raising the secondary voltage. This principle was first successfully utilized by Dr. Donald W. Kerst to produce a device known as the induction accelerator or betatron. In this device, electrons injected into a doughnut-shaped evacuated glass tube placed between the pole-faces of an alternating-current electro magnet, are accelerated by means of the changing magnetic field. This field not only accelerates them, but constrains them to move in an almost circular orbit. As their velocity increases, however, with each orbit, their path gradually spirals outward until they finally collide with a metal target placed within and near the wall of the tube, and produce x-rays.

Dr. Kerst's first betatron, made at the University of Illinois, yielded two-and-a-half-million-volt x-rays. As Dr. Coolidge was very much interested in this, he arranged with the university for the loan of Dr. Kerst, so that with his help and that of Charlton and Westendorp, and with the Research Laboratory facilities, a larger betatron could be built. This machine was completed in fifteen months and proved capable of producing twenty-million-volt x-rays. It was then loaned to the University, and Dr. Kerst returned to the physics department there.

With the enthusiastic support of Charles E. Wilson, then president of the General Electric Company, it was decided that the Research Laboratory should build a really large betatron, capable of producing one-hundred-million-volt x-rays. It was a costly undertaking, involving the erection of a special building with thick radiation-absorbing walls to house it. The work was headed by Charlton and Westendorp and was successfully completed in one year. This machine has been in almost constant use ever since, for research purposes—smashing atoms, generating neutrons and producing other nuclear phenomena. It has also been used for biological studies and for experimental radiographic work.

Studies were being made during this period of the characteristics of electrical discharges in various gases at pressures ranging from one to over one hundred atmospheres. Dr. C. G. Suits directed this activity. In a talk given to the engineers at the General Electric River Works, Lynn, Massachusetts, Coolidge explained the nature of this project.

"He (Dr. Suits) first needed to know the temperature of the arc. This knowledge he obtained indirectly through measurement of sound velocity through the arc. He next wanted to know the voltage gradient in the arc. This could not be obtained by simply dividing the total voltage by the length of the arc, as the total voltage included the drop at the electrode surfaces. By giving one of the electrodes a vibratory motion of known amplitude in the direction of the axis of the arc, he produced a small alternating electro-motive-force which could be amplified, and in this way, obtained the true voltage along the arc. Through the results of these and other measurements, he has been able to make important generalizations concerning the characteristics of arcs—generalizations certain to be helpful in our various arc lighting, arc welding and current interrupting problems."

Metallurgists of the laboratory were working on an alloy of iron, nickel and cobalt, called Fernico, which would have the same heat expansion over a wide range as a certain glass, that could be used in large glass-to-metal seals. The crux of the problem was the difficulty in duplicating the product with sufficient exactness because of the oxidation taking place in the furnace where the alloy was cast. Eventually a solution of the problem was found through the use of a pressed-powder method of producing the ingots.

An investigation of the orientation of individual crystals in magnetic material was specially helpful in connection with transformer steel. Through earlier work the laboratory had been able to produce very large crystals in this material and to study the magnetic properties in various directions in the crystal. This work had indicated that, at the densities used in transformers, permeability was considerably greater in the direction of the edges of the elementary cubes of the iron space lattice than in other directions. This meant that, if, in the course of rolling the steel ingot, the millions of constituent crystal grains could be given a proper orientation, the permeability of the strips used in the transformer could be increased in the direction of their length. The net result was a lighter and cheaper transformer than it had ever before been possible to build.

By the middle 1930's business had largely recovered from the depression. The work of the Research Laboratory had expanded into many new fields. Some three hundred people were employed, of whom about one hundred were research workers. Its budget was over a million dollars a year. It had outgrown its quarters in Building 5 of the Schenectady Works and included also a large part of Building 37, an adjacent structure built in the 1920's. Its main objective continued to be fundamental research to develop important new physical facts and principles. But a certain amount of application work was unavoidable.

As Coolidge expressed it, "Research on applications of existing knowledge yields better and lower cost products and new fields of use for those products, but only fundamental research can give the new knowledge which makes possible radically new things." He sometimes wished that the laboratory might do nothing except fundamental research, but concluded that this was an unattainable ideal for a laboratory located in close proximity to large and active engineering and manufacturing groups.

The fame of the Research Laboratory had spread far and wide, though few people understood exactly how it functioned. Early in 1939, Dr. Coolidge was called to testify before the Temporary National Economic Committee of the Congress of the United States studying certain aspects of production and distribution of goods and services. After he had identified himself as director of the Research Laboratory of the General Electric Company, an exchange of questions and answers took place.

Mr. Dienner.　Am I correct in understanding that was the first industrial research laboratory in the United States?

Dr. Coolidge.　So far as I know: yes, sir.

Mr. Dienner.　It is identified in popular language as the House of Magic; is it not?

Dr. Coolidge.　Yes.

The Chairman.　This is the successor of Mr. Steinmetz?

Dr. Coolidge.　You might regard it as such. But it might be interesting for me to say a few words as to how this laboratory happened to be formed. (He then described the establishment of the laboratory.)

The Chairman.　Would it be inappropriate if we would call it the brain trust of the General Electric Company?

Dr. Coolidge.　I think a little, because some of our people would feel that there were brains outside of the laboratory.

The discussion continued with a description of the work of the laboratory and data showing the extent to which the public benefited from its research activities.

Not long afterward Coolidge went to Springfield, Massachusetts, to receive the Faraday Medal of the Institution of Electrical Engineers of England; "For notable scientific or industrial achievement in electrical engineering." Only two other Americans had previously received this award.

In making the presentation, Dr. Gano Dunn, the Institution's honorary secretary for the United States pointed out, "The Faraday Medal is like the laurel wreath of the Greeks. It is of bronze rather than gold, because it was particularly desired that there should be no suggestion of intrinsic value in the medal itself, but should owe its value, first to the fact that it was instituted to commemorate the foundation of the Institution of Electrical Engineers, and second that it is offered for world-wide service to electrical science and electrical engineering."

Coolidge, in his acceptance address, stated that "This award by a British institution to an American is one more bit of evidence that science knows no national boundary lines." Continuing, he said:

"I feel that I truly owe an acknowledgement to Michael Faraday, for his fundamental researches were an effective stimulus to the conception of our laboratory. Not only can the origin of many General Electric products be traced directly to his work, such as our generators and transformers, which are the engineering derivatives of his classic discovery of electromagnetic induction, but, since economical generation and distribution of electric power have made possible the development of our great electrical industry, it may truly be said that our company owes its existence, as part of that industry, to Faraday's experiments. . . . We are still actively interested in the sparks and arc-discharges with which Faraday worked. It is only the dimensions which have changed. Our latest impulse generator produces ten-million-volt sparks thirty feet long; while another impulse generator, for high current, delivers a quarter of a million amperes—more current than has ever been measured in a lightning stroke."

With the outbreak of World War II in Europe, the United States, although not an active participant, began to give increased attention to national defense. As part of this program, Secretary of Commerce Harry Hopkins organized a National Inventor's Council of fifteen members to encourage civilian inventions of value to the country's defense. Coolidge was one of those selected. Enormous quantities of mail poured in to the council with suggestions. One small-town grocer submitted plans for a large battle cruiser capable of taking off into the air if attacked. But he had no plan for the engine. Many of the suggestions were useful, however, and some were brilliant. Periodic meetings were held by the council, one at the Mohawk Club in Schenectady with Coolidge as host.

One of the most significant of Coolidge's activities in the period immediately preceding the entry of the United States was service on President Roosevelt's Advisory Committee on Uranium. A number of American scientists had been extremely interested in the progress that had been made in using neutron bombardment to split the atom of a special form of uranium known as "U235" with the release of an enormous quantity of energy and also more neutrons. They thought that it might be possible to set up a chain reaction which would provide the general pattern for an atomic bomb.

The crux of the problem was to find a way to obtain a sizable quantity of U235 which was then available only in microscopic amounts. In 1940 Professor A. O. Nier of the University of Minnesota, as well as Dr. K. H. Kingdon and Dr. H. C. Pollock of the G.E. Research Laboratory had independently succeeded in isolating tiny amounts of U235, but the quantities were measured in hundred-millionths of a gram. A method of making much larger amounts would be needed if practical results were to be achieved.

When a group of scientists explained this situation to the President, he acted promptly by appointing an advisory committee of six to evaluate the military importance of the uranium problem and to recommend the level of expenditure at which the problem should be investigated.

Impetus was given to the committee's investigation by the report that Germany was pushing atomic research with great vigor. By the fall of 1941, the imminence of war between Japan and the United States had become widely recognized. Consultations were held with British scientists who had been working along similar lines. In the latter part of November the Advisory Committee on

Uranium reported to President Roosevelt that there was a good possibility of obtaining atomic bombs for use in the impending war and urged an all-out effort for their development. It was also recommended that the existing committee be reorganized for enlarged activity. On the day before Pearl Harbor a decision was reached to undertake the all-out effort, and the work was placed under the jurisdiction of the Office of Scientific Research and Development.

World War II had a much more profound effect on the Research Laboratory than had World War I. This time the national government realized more clearly the potential power of research and mobilized the country's research facilities more effectively. The United States had scarcely become an active participant in the war before the Research Laboratory was devoting itself almost one hundred percent to war work. As director of the laboratory, and also, since 1940, vice-president in charge of research for the entire company, Coolidge carried a heavy burden of responsibility. Valuable assistance in his administrative work was provided by Larry Hawkins, executive engineer of the laboratory, and by his secretary Mary Christie.

The largest single group in the laboratory was engaged in work on radar and radar countermeasures. The story of radar in the war was a story of a race against time. Whatever some scientists did, other scientists tried to undo. In this race, American and British scientists far outdistanced the Germans and the Japanese. It can be said without danger of contradiction that the United

Nations had radar and made the most of it; the Axis also had radar, but, because of Allied countermeasures, got comparatively little out of it.

At the very start, the army and navy asked the National Defense Research Committee to undertake a study of the whole field of radar interference and countermeasures. The Germans were developing their radar and it became evident that a great effort must be made to neutralize or weaken it if the Allied air raids on Germany were not to become prohibitively costly in lives and in planes. To meet this situation, Division 15 of N.D.R.C. was organized under Dr. C. G. Suits of the laboratory, with headquarters at Schenectady. Originally its staff numbered about two hundred, but in a short time, it had grown to more than one thousand physicists and engineers in laboratories all over the country.

Back in 1921, Dr. Albert W. Hull of the laboratory had invented a new electronic tube called a "magnetron." This produced radio waves of very high frequency, like those employed in radar, and of considerable power. With certain adaptations this device became an extremely effective means of jamming enemy radar. The laboratory developed a complete line of magnetrons of high power covering a wide range of frequencies. This equipment was flown to England and put to immediate use. In this way about eighty percent of the German, radar-controlled antiaircraft batteries were jammed out of operation, and the loss of Allied planes was greatly reduced.

On one Saturday afternoon in the fall of 1944, the

navy came to the Research Laboratory with an urgent request for a new electronic tube to operate in a jamming transmitter at a frequency different from the magnetron then in use. Ten of the new jammers, plus spares, were wanted for installation on battleships within a week.

Experiments were started at once for the purpose of developing a tube of this kind. Fortunately it was found that the tube previously used could be redesigned to have the proper characteristics. In addition to the tubes, however, other parts were needed. These included new antennas keyed to the new frequency, transmitter modification parts and dummy antennas to tune the new devices without creating a signal. Equipment for the entire ten sets was ready on the morning of the ninth day after the request was received. That afternoon the equipment was picked up by a navy plane and flown to the Pacific for use against Japanese bombers.

Smoke was another protective device upon which the Research Laboratory was able to render assistance of great value. It was realized that in the Allied landings which were eventually to be made in Africa, Europe and the Japanese-held islands of the Pacific, many lives could be saved if more effective smoke screens could be produced. The Chemical Warfare Service enlisted the aid of Irving Langmuir on this project. He decided that the first thing to do was to determine definitely the most effective size, density and color of smoke particles. After this had been determined, five different models of smoke generators were built before one was found that would turn out the proper smoke particle, a liquid globule of microscopic proportions. These generators were so effective that a small number of them correctly placed could mask an entire city. The army pronounced them "the greatest life-saver of our troops."

Demands for tungsten increased steadily as the war progressed. It has been estimated that this metal was used in 15,000 different types of war items. The largest supply of high-grade tungsten ore came from China, where it had been discovered accidentally by a young scientist, K. C. Li, in 1911. But this source was cut off by the Japanese even before the United States became a participant, and General Electric, as the country's largest user of tungsten, undertook research in methods of processing off-grade ores in order to secure adequate quantities for the needs of this emergency. To Coolidge, who had worked so long and hard on the production of ductile tungsten, this research activity was particularly interesting.

In 1948, K. C. Li established the K. C. Li Medal and Prize "for meritorious achievement in advancing the science of tungsten," to be administered by the Trustees of Columbia University. The first recipient of this award, in 1952, was Dr. William David Coolidge.

Second in size only to the Research Laboratory group working on radar and countermeasures was that engaged in the development of silicone rubber. For a number of years the laboratory's chemists had been conducting research in the curious chemical compounds known as "silicones." A principal constituent of these is silicon, the element present in such common things as glass and sand. Chemically speaking, silicon is quite similar to carbon, a major ingredient of natural and synthetic rubber. Both silicon and carbon can form long, chain-like molecules, called "polymers." Silicon polymers, however, have much greater thermal stability than carbon polymers. Making use of this characteristic, the Research Laboratory developed a new material called "silicone rubber" having many of the qualities of natural rubber and certain additional advantages. It was widely used by both the army and the navy for gaskets, shock absorbers, and for various other purposes.

Other results of silicon research were numerous types of silicon resins, oils and greases characterized by being remarkably stable under a wide variety of conditions and temperatures. "Dri-film" was a water repellant having important applications for insulators in communication equipment and in making canisters for gas masks. Alkyd resin paints were developed to replace linseed oil and varnish paints for faster drying and greater durability for ships.

As there was imperative need for rapid inspection of both materials and finished products, x-ray equipment was in great demand. To meet this demand the Research Laboratory and the G.E. X-ray Corporation worked in close cooperation. One-million-volt x-ray machines of the general type developed in 1939 were made for war production plants all over the country. Many of them operated day and night. Besides inspecting the materials used for war purposes, they were the only practical way of culling out defective shells, which, because of inadequate filling with TNT, might have exploded in gun barrels. Development of the two-million-volt x-ray unit in 1944 made it possible for the first time to radiograph steel of 12-inch thickness. Used on 8-inch steel, it was one hundred times faster than the one-million-volt unit.

In many other fields than those mentioned, the research laboratory also made important contributions. The vast multiplicity and diversity of war projects offered full scope for utilizing the experience and special knowledge of every individual in the laboratory. With his administrative duties and outside consulting work for such agencies as the National Inventor's Council, the National Defense Research Committee and others, Coolidge had no time for direct personal participation in the laboratory's projects but he gave continuing guidance and encouragement.

REFERENCES

Charlton, E. C., unpublished interview

Coolidge, William D., "Experiences with the X-Ray Tube," American Journal of Roentgenology and Radium Therapy, December, 1945

————Faraday Medal Acceptance Address before the Northeastern District Meeting, A.I.E.E., Springfield, Mass., May 4, 1939

————Statement before the Temporary National Economic Committee of the Congress of the United States, Washington, D. C., January, 1939

———Unpublished talk before the Engineering Society of the General Electric River Works, Lynn, Mass., October 4, 1937

Hawkins, Laurence A., *Adventure into the Unknown*
William Morrow & Co., 1950

Li, K. C., and Chung Yu Wang—*Tungsten, Its History, Geology, Ore-Dressing, Metallurgy, Chemistry, Analysis, Applications and Economics,* American Chemical Society Monograph No. 94, third edition, Rheinhold Publishing Corporation, 1955

Miller, John A., *Men and Volts at War,* McGraw-Hill, 1947

13

Host to V.I.P.'s

Explaining what it called the benevolent appearance of W. D. Coolidge, an article in the April 1931 issue of *World's Work* said that it came "from his eyes, which are kindly, and from his anxiety to see that every visitor to the laboratory obtains whatever he is seeking."

The task of taking care of visitors has always been a serious responsibility of the officials of the research laboratory. At the time Coolidge became director, these visitors numbered about fifteen thousand a year. Many, of course, came to see individual scientists about something in the particular field in which the visitor was interested. Many, too, came because of general curiosity about the laboratory, and these could be handled by the specially trained guides employed for that purpose. But there were many others, people of distinction in the scientific world, or in business and industry, government officials, high-ranking officers of the army and navy, foreigners who had heard of the laboratory's remarkable achievements, and others, whom the director or one of the associate directors wished to entertain personally.

"Among the great whom I have met and admired," Coolidge says, "I must give a high place to Madame Marie Curie. It was in connection with her visit to this country in 1929 that I first met her. This visit was conducted by the late Mrs. William Brown Meloney, of the *New York Herald Tribune*. Following her visit to Dearborn, Madame Curie wished to visit the Research Laboratory of the General Electric Company in Schenectady.

"She was to travel here by train, and hotel reservations had been made in Schenectady, and plans had been made by Polish friends here for welcoming their distinguished compatriot. At the last moment, a telegram was received from Mrs. Meloney, requesting that all previous arrangements be cancelled, and that Madame Curie be taken off the train in Amsterdam, and thence taken by auto to Schenectady, and there, secretly, to the home of some G.E. official.

"We were told that Madame Curie was ill. We were also told that compatriots at Dearborn had been so eager for mementos of her, that even her laundry disappeared, when sent out, and that she had been badly frightened by having one admirer there, tear off a piece of the coat she was wearing.

"I was privileged, in company with the late Robert Peare, then head of our publicity department, to meet her at Amsterdam. Mr. Peare was, at the time, living at some distance from Schenectady—too far for her convenience in visiting the laboratory. So the privilege of entertaining Madame Curie fell to the lot of Mrs. Coolidge and myself. Furthermore, we were to have her all to ourselves, as no one else was to know where she was staying.

"Arrived at our home, I ran to the door and called out to Dorothy that Madame Curie was here. Dorothy was so sure that I was joking, that I had difficulty in convincing her that I wasn't. She was a bit unprepared, but quickly rose to the occasion.

"There were complications, as our guest facilities are limited, and my parents were visiting us at the time. I can't remember where Dorothy and I slept, but Madame Curie was immediately put to bed in our room, where she stayed for three days. A doctor-friend was sworn to secrecy, and called to attend her. While she was confined to our house, no one but the doctor, Mr. Rice, and Dr. Whitney were told where she was. To show how effective our secrecy measures were: my secretary, in the middle of the night, received a telephone call from a New York newspaper reporter, who wanted to know of Madame Curie's whereabouts; but she was unable to help him, as she didn't know. It still seems remarkable to me, that it was possible to have Madame Curie in our house, right here in the city, for three days, without having her presence known, especially as the original preparations for her visit had been well publicized. She was finally able to make a visit to the Laboratory, during which she was, of course, carefully shielded from anything but the few personal contacts which she especially wanted to make. Following this, Mr. Owen D. Young took her by auto, to Canton, New York to dedicate the new Hepburn Hall of Chemistry of St. Lawrence University.

"In 1933, with Dorothy, I visited Madame Curie's laboratory in Paris. We had just come from a visit to Russia, which we had entered through Poland. Madame Curie hung on every word that we could say about her homeland. She then wanted Dorothy to accompany herself and me on a trip through her laboratory; but Dorothy demurred, saying that she wasn't a scientist, wouldn't understand what she saw, and would only cause delay. Madame Curie responded by putting her arm around her, taking no refusal, and drawing her along. In Schenectady, her illness had kept us from feeling the warmth of her nature, which revealed itself to us so strongly and unforgettably in Paris. I hadn't realized it before, but she was not only charming, but very beautiful."

The visitors' roster of the laboratory is sprinkled with the names of famous people who visited there: Coolidge's classmate, G. K. Burgess of the U.S. Bureau of Standards, Arthur Compton from Princeton, Assistant Secretary of the Navy Warner, Sir Charles Parsons, inventor of the Parsons steam turbine, Admiral Straus of the United States Navy, Guiseppe Marconi, Sir Ernest Rutherford, Niels Bohr, Charles Lindbergh, Sir J. J. Thompson, Dr. Francis Williams, a pioneer radiologist of Boston, Andre Maurois, Harvey S. Firestone, Jr., Robert A. Millikan, Percy W. Bridgman, A. A. Michelson, Harlow Shapley, Hussein Sabry Pascha, uncle of the King of Egypt, Grover

Whalen, president of the New York World's Fair, and innumerable others.

Charles Kettering visited the laboratory on a number of occasions besides the time he came to assist with the generator for the army's portable x-ray unit. He had a keen sense of humor and Coolidge enjoyed listening to stories of his pranks. One of his favorite stories was about an ancient Stevens-Duryca automobile he had once owned. He decided to try a Hall-Scott airplane engine in place of the car's regular Stevens-Duryea engine, and had the change made secretly in a barn at Dayton.

Shortly afterward the local sales representative of the Stevens-Duryea company came to see him to try to interest him in buying a new car. Kettering demurred, saying that the old car was still pretty good. Not at all discouraged, the agent said he would like to demonstrate the superiority of the new model.

It was agreed that they should meet for a test run on a stretch of road outside the city. This they did, starting the cars together; but Kettering's old car quickly forged ahead and was soon lost to the agent's sight. On the telephone the next day, the agent asked what had been done to that old car. Just a little adjustment of the carburetor, Kettering told him.

This jokesome tendency on the part of Kettering once nearly disrupted the operation of General Electric's television station WRGB. One of the earliest programs of this station was a discussion on science and research between

Coolidge and Kettering. Both of them had been out in the sun a good deal and were deeply tanned. To keep them from looking like blackface comedians, it was considered necessary to apply a good deal of make-up. Neither liked this idea very much, but they finally agreed to it. But Kettering absolutely refused to submit a script so that the master of ceremonies could time his show. At a warm-up session in the late afternoon he tried to plan his questions so that they would lead to the expected answers. Kettering, however, was not content merely to answer the questions, but rambled on about a variety of subjects. Nevertheless, a time schedule was worked out.

In the evening, when the show was actually on the air, the master of ceremonies was horrified to hear Kettering talking about entirely different things and knocking the time schedule into a cocked hat. Later it was learned that Kettering was perfectly aware of the time element and was keeping his eye on the clock so that the show would actually conclude on scheduled time. The master of ceremonies, however, barely survived the ordeal.

General Electric was broadcasting also a weekly program called "The Science Forum" over its radio station WGY. Many prominent people came to Schenectady to take part in this program, and it was the custom to invite scientists from the research laboratory to have dinner with the speakers before the broadcasts. There was a standing rule that, when Coolidge was among the guests from the laboratory, a dinner of lamb chops and green peas should be ordered for him regardless of the menu for the rest of the party. Considerable speculation took place about the reason for this rule, whether it was a special diet he observed, or whether there was some more obscure reason for it. The simple fact was, however, that he liked chops and peas.

"I shall never forget," Coolidge says, "one of the many pleasant visits we in our laboratory enjoyed with Dr. Kenneth Mees who started the research laboratory of the Eastman Kodak Company, and for many years served as vice-president and director. On the visit I have in mind he showed us his company's brand-new development—a 16-millimeter moving picture camera. This seemed a very appealing tool for the amateur photographer, but Dr. Mees said that the Kodak salesmen felt it was too expensive to be sold successfully. The error of this reasoning was indicated when Whitney, Langmuir and I each bought one of these cameras. Dr. Mees was delighted to go home with three firm orders to show his company's salesmen as evidence of the salability of the new camera."

When Cyrus McCormick of the International Harvester Company visited the laboratory, he and Coolidge had a long talk about conditions in Russia. The Russians were buying harvesting equipment from the Harvester Company at this time, but they were also trying to learn how to make the equipment for themselves. McCormick was not much impressed by their efforts. They had no mechanical sense, he thought. As evidence of this, he said the Harvester Company would send them crates of ball bearings, only for the Russians to let them stand in the rain where they were soon ruined by rust. "When you think of what the Russians have since accomplished in the air and in space," Coolidge says, "it seems that mechanical skill can be acquired very rapidly."

Henry Ford once took a tour through the laboratory under Coolidge's guidance. As they walked along the corridors glancing through the open doors into the workrooms where the scientists were carrying on their various activities, Mr. Ford had little to say. At the end of the tour he asked, "Do you like having men working in these little cubicles?" This, to him, was the most interesting thing he had seen. Some time later, when Coolidge visited the laboratory at the main Ford plant, he understood better the reason for the question. The whole laboratory was one very large room with no partitions. Coolidge's first reaction was that it would be impossible to concentrate on a single, technical problem with so much other activity going on all around. On second thought he realized there might be some advantage in having no partitions in the laboratory of an automobile manufacturing concern. An entire automobile, or any part of one could be brought comparatively easily to any place in the laboratory. This, he realized, would not be possible where the scientists worked in what Mr. Ford called "little cubicles."

Medical men were prominent among the visitors. Speaking at the sesquicentennial celebration of the Medical Society of the County of Schenectady in 1960, Dr. Ellis Kellert said: "During the past half century, many physicians from all over the world have visited Schenectady, not to see our historic sites nor to visit our excellent hospitals. They have come to see William D. Coolidge, Ph.D., and his new marvelous tungsten target x-ray tube that has advanced medical diagnosis so markedly and has made deep x-ray therapy possible."

Playing host to important visitors made sizable inroads on his time, Coolidge found, but he never begrudged it. "In the long run," he says, "we, in the laboratory have benefited as much from our visitors as they have by what they saw and learned from us."

REFERENCES

Coolidge, William D., "Autobiographical Notes," manuscript
_____digest of his laboratory notebooks
Kellert, Ellis, "Medical Memorabilia of Old Schenectady," address before the Medical Society of the County of Schenectady, June 2, 1960
Tanis, Hubert, "Retirement Remarks," Research Laboratory Notes #17, Dec. 5, 1962

14

Adventure in Retirement

Having passed the usual retirement age, Coolidge was contemplating giving up his job as director of the Research Laboratory shortly before the beginning of World War II. When war was declared, however, he found that he must postpone this step. The management of the company told him that his services would be essential to the war effort, and he consented to remain. With the successful conclusion of the war in sight in the latter part of 1944, he renewed his plans for retirement. As his successor he proposed Dr. C. Guy Suits, who before the war had proved his exceptional ability in physical research, and during the war had demonstrated, as chief of Division 15 of N.D.R.C., his executive ability in the administration of a large research organization. "He understands and appreciates both fundamental and applied research," Coolidge said of Dr. Suits at his retirement dinner, "as well as the scientific approach to a problem. He comes from our own ranks, and takes pride in our traditions."

Continuing, he said, "I have been in the research laboratory thirty-nine years—the best and happiest years of my life. As I look back over them there is one thought which dominates and dwarfs all others and that is the thought of how lucky I have been in my associates. It was my luck; but Dr. Whitney's careful hand-picking was responsible."

Though Coolidge retired as vice-president and director of research, he remained as a consultant to the Research Laboratory in x-ray matters, and continued as a consulting engineer of the General Electric X-Ray Corporation.

Not long after his retirement he undertook a two-month's airplane trip to South America to assist medical and other groups in the celebration of the fiftieth anniversary of Roentgen's discovery of x-rays. Mrs. Coolidge accompanied him.

The first stop after leaving Miami, Florida, was at Lima, Peru. There Coolidge spoke at the University of San Marcos, the oldest university in the Western Hemisphere. While in Lima they had an opportunity to visit the museum with its remarkable collection of ancient Inca pottery and textiles—the latter with very beautiful color combinations.

Then they proceeded to Santiago, Chile, where, at the University of Chile, Coolidge received the "Orden al Merito" (Order of Merit) of the Chilean government for "his many contributions to civilization." The award was conferred at a reception tendered by the faculties of medicine, physics and mathematics.

Schenectady Union Star Photograph

Dr. and Mrs. Coolidge viewing pictures taken on their travels

As Dr. Armando Larraguibel, dean of the faculty of medicine, placed the jewel of the order around Dr. Coolidge's neck, he said:

"The scientists of Chile have delegated me to give you this jewel, which is made of the gold of the Chilean mountains and by Chilean hands, and it represents the kindest love of the Chilean people."

Dr. Larraguibel and Senor Pablo Krassa, deans of the faculties of physics and mathematics, also gave him diplomas as honorary member of their faculties. The Catholic university gave him an honorary diploma and he was made an honorary member of the Chilean Radiological society.

At Cordoba, Argentina, Will and Dorothy attended the opening of a new x-ray clinic under the auspices of Dr. de Rienzo. Montevideo, Uruguay, was the next stop for the opening of an x-ray exposition in that city. This was to have been opened by Uruguay's President Amazaga, but he asked Mrs. Coolidge to take his place in cutting the ribbon that had been stretched across the entrance.

In Brazil the Coolidges were the guests of the Brazilian Government at the Copacabana in Rio de Janeiro. Will received an honorary doctor's degree from the University of San Paulo and another from the National School of Engineering, a component of the University of Brazil. The latter degree was one of only two which the institution had ever given; the other was to Mme. Curie. At Bahia the Coolidges attended the opening of the new x-ray clinic of Dr. Adelaido Ribeiro, Will being asked to declare it officially open.

"In all of the cities we visited," Coolidge says, "we were very graciously received. Large groups met us at the airports when we arrived, which was often very early in the morning, and were there to wish us 'good-bye' when we left, which was often very late at night."

When the atom bomb test, "Operations Crossroads," was held in the summer of 1946 at Bikini Atoll in the Pacific, Coolidge was invited to attend as a special representative of the Manhattan Project of the Corps of Engineers, U.S. Army. Leaving Washington by plane on June 23, the party had a one-day stop-over in Hawaii before proceeding to Bikini lagoon, where a group of warships had been assembled for the test. The obsolete battleship, U.S.S. *Nevada,* was in the center directly below the point where the bomb was to be exploded.

After circling the target area several times, the plane proceeded two hundred and forty miles further to a landing field on Kwajalein Island. Everywhere the destruction of war was evident. Not a live tree was left on the island— only a half-dozen bare and dismembered trunks.

Here Will was intrigued by the sight of many small windmills, each three or four feet in diameter, and located only a few feet above ground. On closer view it developed that each of these was a soldier's or sailor's homemade power plant for an individual clothes washing machine, consisting of the windmill, a galvanized iron can, and a mechanism for translating rotary into reciprocating motion and so swashing the clothes up and down in the wash-water in the can.

After a tour of Kwajalein, the party went on board a destroyer and returned to Bikini where they were transferred to a larger ship, the seaplane tender, U.S.S. *Cumberland Sound,* which served as their home during the test period.

A visit was made next day to a number of the target ships so that the observers would have a basis for comparison when they inspected them after the dropping of the bomb.

On board the *Cumberland Sound,* Will shared a stateroom with A. W. Robertson, chairman of the board of the Westinghouse Electric Corporation. This afforded him a most interesting opportunity to see the General Electric Company through the eyes of one of its competitors.

Early on the morning of July first, the *Cumberland Sound* pulled up anchor and took the party away from the target area to a distance of about nineteen miles, far enough so that only the masts of the target ships were visible above the horizon.

Reporting his observations on the G.E. "Science Forum," Coolidge said:

"Equipped with special, very dark glasses to protect our eyes from the first dazzling flash, and with binoculars for subsequent use, we awaited anxiously the event which we had come nearly 8000 miles to see. There was first the brilliant flash of light attended by a definite feeling of warmth of the face. One observer quickly turned and compared this feeling of warmth with that obtained from the sun and found it of about the same intensity. The noise of the explosion, traveling with the velocity of sound, reached us in about one and a half minutes after the visible flash, and was just a single dull boom."

On the day after the explosion, the *Cumberland Sound* returned to Bikini lagoon and the party was able on succeeding days to visit four of the target ships, the battleships *Nevada* and *Arkansas,* the heavy cruiser *Pensacola* and the German cruiser *Prinz Eugen.* They saw extensive damage to superstructures on all of these ships, except the *Prinz Eugen* which was farthest away from the bomb, but even her radar equipment had suffered.

Two transports, two destroyers, and a Japanese cruiser had been sunk. A submarine had been so badly damaged that it would not have been able to submerge. The test had been well planned to show what the air-burst bomb would do at various distances. Objects of many kinds, including live ammunition, as well as live animals had been placed on the decks of the ships to determine the effects of the blast.

The observers could, of course, form only hasty and superficial conclusions concerning the extent of the damage, which was later surveyed with great care by armed services personnel. Nevertheless it was the general conclusion that the test had yielded a mass of information of inestimable value—information that could not have been obtained in any other way .

In the fall of 1946, Coolidge re-entered the employ of the General Electric Company for a period of four months to establish a small branch of the Schenectady Research Laboratory at Richland, Washington, where the company operated a large plant for the production of plutonium. Accompanied by Mrs. Coolidge and about a dozen scientists from the research laboratory, he traveled by chartered plane leaving from the Albany airport in the morning.

As the plane was passing over Great Salt Lake it became evident that it was heading directly into a severe thunderstorm. The pilot assured the passengers that there would be no danger in going through the storm, but that it would probably be pretty uncomfortable traveling. He asked if they would like to put back to Salt Lake City and spend the night there. A decision was reached that this would be more sensible than going on, and a little later the entire party found themselves comfortably settled in a large motel on the outskirts of the city.

For this the G.E. local manager was largely responsible, as the Mormon Church was holding a convention in the city and the Coolidge party would have had a hard time finding accommodations without his aid. As a reward for his efforts, the manager asked if he might arrange for a little local publicity about the stopover of the group of scientists.

Not content with a general story, the reporter for a morning paper requested a personal interview with the distinguished Dr. Coolidge. This request was not unexpected, but Coolidge, who was just recovering from a bout of influenza had asked W. H. Milton, Jr. to pinch hit for him. Milton explained the situation and gave the reporter full information about the party and the purpose of the trip. The reporter accepted this information, though still dissatisfied that he had been unable to talk personally to Coolidge.

Across the front page of the paper the next morning ran the headline, "Thirteen Prominent Scientists Grounded Here." The article went on to tell the general purpose of the trip and give all available biographical information about the research laboratory men in the group. At the end the reporter added, "Dr. W. D. Coolidge was also in the party."

The plant at Richland had been built for the United States Government during World War II by the du Pont Company, which had later withdrawn from its operation, with General Electric taking over the responsibility. Security and safety precautions were of paramount importance. When visiting the plant during the war, scientists and engineers had had to use assumed names such as Smith and Jones to prevent their identities becoming known.

Knowing a good deal about radiation hazards, Coolidge was much impressed by the many effective precautions which had been taken to protect the workers in the plant from the tremendous amount of radioactivity in the great piles and in the chemical processing of the output of these piles. It was extremely fortunate, he thought, that this activity had been preceded by such extensive medical application of x-rays and radium. For, through the therapeutic use of these radiations, their effects on living tissues had been learned and methods of dosage measurement had been developed. Protective measures in the plant extended not only to normal operation, but also to the rapid removal of personnel in case of danger resulting from apparatus failure.

The population of Richland during the Coolidges' stay consisted very largely of young engineers and chemists and their families. As a result the average age of the inhabitants was about six years. Dorothy noticed some children playing one day near the house and heard one of them ask, looking at her, "Who is she?" Another answered, "She's a grandmother"—something almost without precedent at Richland.

Because the town was quite remote from any large city, the inhabitants had to provide their own entertainment. In this they were extremely resourceful. At social gatherings everyone had to do his bit. If instrumental music was in order, and he couldn't use anything else, he had to play on a comb.

The Coolidges' house, which was owned and furnished by General Electric, was located close to the Columbia River. The natural scenery of the area presented a constant challenge to the photographer. Particularly interesting were the flocks of wild geese along the river bank close to the house. While the job of setting up the branch laboratory occupied most of Will's time, he managed in the intervals to do a good bit of photography, developing and printing his pictures in the basement photographic laboratory that had been provided for him. Altogether the four months at Richland passed quickly and pleasantly and both Will and Dorothy were almost sorry when the time came to return to Schenectady.

Six months after his return from Richland, Coolidge was asked by the National Academy of Sciences to be one of a group of six to visit Japan and advise members of General MacArthur's staff concerning plans for the reorganization of science and technology in that country. The group assembled at San Francisco and were flown to Tokyo by the Army Transport Command. All arrangements in Japan were in the hands of the American Military Government. Accommodations were provided for them at the Imperial Hotel in Tokyo and a special train placed at their disposal for trips to other cities. Visits were paid to the laboratories of various universities, the government and industry, where conferences were held with Japanese scientists.

The devastating effects of the war on the national economy were everywhere in evidence. A large part of the industrial machine had been destroyed and what was left was out of date and in poor repair. Food was scarce, and the Japanese scientists, like all other workers, had to devote much of their efforts simply to getting enough to eat.

The American group came to the conclusion that the final decisions concerning the organization and support of science in Japan would have to be made by the Japanese themselves. It was the feeling, however, that the many conferences and discussions between the scientists of the two countries had resulted in clarifying the situation for all of them and had thus been of considerable benefit.

On this trip, lasting forty days in Japan, there were some interesting interludes. One of these was a visit to the laboratory of Mr. Mikimoto, the discoverer of the method of making culture pearls. At the conclusion of the visit, each of the Americans was presented with three "graduate" oysters, apparently selected at random. "I suspect," Coolidge says, "that something other than chance had played a role, perhaps the x-ray fluoroscope, for all of the members of our party fared surprisingly well."

As a permanent tribute to Coolidge, the largest x-ray development laboratory in the world was dedicated at Milwaukee on September 13, 1948. Built by the General Electric X-Ray Corporation, the new William D. Coolidge Laboratory represented the culmination of an expansion program launched more than two years earlier in an effort to keep pace with the growing use of x-ray equipment in medicine and industry. The ceremonies were witnessed by more than one thousand distinguished visitors, many of them brought by special train from Chicago. Dorothy went with Will to the dedication.

"It is recognized by everyone acquainted with the work of Dr. Coolidge," Dr. Arthur Christie, world-famous radiologist, said in his dedication address, "that his inventions and discoveries have contributed immeasurably to the progress of medicine. Who can estimate the effects

*Dr. Christie and Dr. Coolidge at the dedication of the Coolidge
Laboratory*

upon human welfare and medical progress of one of his earliest achievements of forty years ago, when in his youth he devised a method to render tungsten ductile, and thus made possible the modern incandescent lamp? The medals and honors bestowed upon Dr. Coolidge by universities, physical institutes and scientific societies throughout the world have recognized, repeatedly, not only his basic scientific discoveries and inventions, but also his contributions to the science and art of medicine. . . . We pay our tribute to our honored friend today as a successful searcher after truth. Beyond that, we honor him as a humanitarian, that is, one whose life and work have added to the sum total of human welfare and happiness."

The audience sensed, according to one who was present, that here was a man whose epic discoveries merited even more than a memorial building of stone, filled with scientific equipment. Here was a man who, because of his great work, belonged to the whole world—a benefactor of humanity and "a kindly, modest, unpretentious man."

Additional recognition of Coolidge's work was received in 1949 when the Philosophical Faculty of the University of Leipzig presented him with a renewal of his Doctor-Diploma received in 1899 and congratulated him on the golden anniversary of the original presentation.

Anyone in Schenectady making a casual inquiry as to the whereabouts of Dr. Coolidge is likely to receive the reply, "He is probably on a trip around the world." This may be an exaggeration, but is not entirely without foundation. In 1952 Will and Dorothy visited the Hawaiian Islands, Fiji and New Zealand. The next year they spent three months in Africa. A Mediterranean cruise was taken in 1955, a tour of Greece and Italy the next year, a trip to Spain and the Canary Islands in 1958, followed by an around-the-world tour in 1959, and a visit to Scandinavia in 1961.

"Traveling is very educational," Will says, "It certainly makes life more interesting." As a preliminary to an automobile trip the Coolidges planned to make through sparsely settled areas in Mexico, Will took a short mechanic's training course at the local Lincoln service agency. Then he procured sufficient spare parts to provide against virtually any emergency. By the time he had equipped himself with all the spare parts he needed, the trunk of the car was nearly full. To all these preparations Dorothy had paid little attention. On the morning of departure, she opened the car trunk to stow her suitcases only to discover an array of parts that would have done credit to any service station. Nevertheless the trip was a great success.

REFERENCES

Christie, Arthur C., Dedication Address, William D. Coolidge Laboratory, Milwaukee, September 13, 1948
Coolidge, William D., "Autobiographical Notes," manuscript
_____"Observations at Bikini," broadcast from Station WGY, July 17, 1946
_____"Report from Japan," broadcast from Station WGY, October 1, 1947
_____"Trip to South America," unpublished manuscript

15

Science and Industry

The philosophy of the typical American is said to be built on a belief in hard work, common sense and recognition of physical forces, coupled with a faith which, if it isn't silly enough to try to move mountains, is strong enough to tunnel them, or build them as need arises. The story of William David Coolidge is a story of continuing achievements based on this philosophy. But recognition of his achievements has not been confined to those who share his American philosophy. It has extended north, south, east and west throughout the civilized world.

For eight years he struggled with the problem of producing ductile tungsten for lamp filaments — making progress, encountering set backs, and, in the end achieving success. Not content with this achievement, he started immediately to hunt for other uses of tungsten, and developed the Coolidge x-ray tube with its heated tungsten-filament cathode, its tungsten target and its high vacuum. The Coolidge x-ray tube was immeasurably better than any that had gone before, but he quickly turned his attention to making it still better. One advance in scientific knowledge was a stepping stone to the next advance.

Coolidge once described the science laboratory, where such advances are made as "the temple in which we come directly in contact with Nature, herself. Here, to the patient, honest, reverent and open mind she reveals herself. In classical times, scientific questions might all have been referred to the Delphic Oracle, but in scientific laboratories we refer them to Nature, changing experimental conditions until, without breaking her laws, she can give the answer."

This process of extracting Nature's secrets has made tremendous progress in the United States since the day in 1905 when Coolidge joined the infant research laboratory of the General Electric Company. Before that the United States had shown remarkable proficiency in developing industries upon the basis of scientific knowledge that had been revealed in other countries, particularly Germany, France and England, but had not engaged in very extensive scientific research of its own. The half century that followed was to see a great change.

Most of the early work in basic science in the United States was done in universities and research institutes. Coolidge's investigation at the Massachusetts Institute of Technology of the electrical conductivity of aqueous solutions at high temperatures was an example. But the scope of the research work done by the universities was restricted by limited funds. After the establishment of the General Electric Research Laboratory, other industries established similar laboratories and a steadily increasing amount of this country's scientific work came to be done by industry. With the enormous financial support which industry was able to give, progress was greatly accelerated.

Speaking at St. Louis, Missouri, early in 1963, the British scientist, Sir Charles Percy Snow, said that "it sometimes surprises Europeans to realize how much of the pure science of the entire West is being carried out in the United States. Curiously enough, it often surprises Americans, too. At a guess the figure is something like 80 percent, and might easily be higher."

This nation has been very lucky, he indicated, in being an enormous country, and a very rich one. But a major factor in its progress has been the effective use it has made of applied science.

One reason why industrial research in the United States has been so successful, Coolidge believes, is that the work of specialists organized to do fundamental research has been combined with the work of others organized to apply newly discovered facts and principles to the production of new devices and designs.

"No man, without the help of others, can get very far," he says. "Modern research and engineering effort recognizes the importance of cooperative teamwork and organizes for it, selecting carefully the necessary physicists, chemists, mechanics, electricians, glass blowers, etc., for the team. Success in a baseball game may depend largely on the pitcher and catcher, but without good fielders, it is impossible."

Another factor has been the prompt publication of new scientific knowledge. In American industry, scientists have been encouraged to announce their findings to the world rather than to cloak them in secrecy. With new facts and principles available to all, the opportunities for their successful application have been multiplied many times. This, in turn, has encouraged the scientists in their efforts to still further extend the boundaries of human knowledge.

Concurrent with the great advances in science that have been made in the past fifty years there has been a growing realization that far more is yet to be discovered than has already been learned. Truth, Coolidge believes, is not something that is limited and found once and for all, but is forever capable of extension.

Some people have been inclined to blame science for many of the ills that beset the world. Just as there were those in 1895 who saw only harmful effects likely to be produced by Roentgen's x-ray discovery, so there are those today who see only what they believe to be harmful results to follow from scientific progress. To them nuclear fission means only the atom bomb, and like the late Dean Inge, they want to declare a moratorium on science. To Coolidge, this is nonsense. Nuclear fission, to him, means a step toward a better world, the increasing use by man of the things that nature has provided.

"The world is not going to the dogs," he says. "We

mustn't allow ourselves the lazy luxury of being pessimistic about the future. I say lazy advisedly, because, if one allows himself to think that conditions are hopelessly bad, he will not exert himself to try to make them better."

As science progresses, it discovers more and more problems. "Trained minds," he says, "firm character and dauntless courage will be needed to wrestle with the problems of the future, to master their threatening dangers, and to force from them the beginnings of a better, more peaceful and richer world. There has never been a danger to an individual or nation in knowing too much. The danger always comes from knowing too little."

REFERENCES

Coolidge, William D., "The Role of Science Institutions in our Civilization," Founder's Day Address at Ursinus College, 1943
_____Testimony before the Temporary Economic Committee of the Congress of the United States, January 1939
Snow, Sir Charles P., Address at Washington University, St. Louis, Missouri, February 23, 1963
Wilson, Charles E., Address at dedication of Coolidge Laboratory, Milwaukee, Wisconsin, September 13, 1948

Published Papers of Dr. William David Coolidge

Eine Neue Methode zur Demonstration der Elektrischen Drahtwellen, ANNALEN DER PHYSIK UND CHEMIE, Neue Folge Band 67, pp.578-91, 1899

Dielektrische Untersuchungen und Elektrische Drahtwellen, ANNALEN DER PHYSIK UND CHEMIE, Neue Folge Band 69, pp.125-66, 1899

Apparatus for Rapidly Calibrating Voltmeters, (F. A. Laws and W. D. Coolidge) TECHNOLOGY QUARTERLY 15, No. 1, pp.69–73, March, 1902

Electrical Conductivity of Aqueous Solutions at High Temperatures, (with A. A. Noyes) PROCEEDINGS OF THE AMERICAN ACADEMY· OF ARTS AND SCIENCES 39, No. 7, pp.163-219, November, 1903

The Electrical Conductivity of Aqueous Solutions. II. Original Apparatus and Method. Conductivity and Ionization of NaC1 and KC1 up to 306 Degrees, (with A. A. Noyes). III. Later Modifications of the Apparatus and Method, CARNEGIE

INSTITUTE PUBLICATION No. 63, pp.9-55, 59-67, 1908

Ductile Tungsten, TRANSACTIONS OF THE AMERICAN INSTITUTE OF ELECTRICAL ENGINEERS 29, Part 2, pp.961-5, 1910

Ductile Tungsten and Metalfilament Electric Lamps, (with J. Howell and C. F. Scott) ENGINEERING NEWS 64, pp.7-9, July 7, 1910

Some Applications of Wrought Tungsten and Molybdenum, THE JOURNAL OF INDUSTRIAL AND ENGINEERING CHEMISTRY 4, pp. 2-4, January, 1912

Roentgen Ray Research. The Use of Tungsten for the Target, METALLURGICAL AND CHEMICAL ENGINEERING 10, No. 3, p.146, March, 1912

Metallic Tungsten and Some of its Applications, TRANSACTIONS OF THE AMERICAN INSTITUTE OF ELECTRICAL ENGINEERS 31, Part 1, pp.1219-28, 1912

A powerful Roentgen Ray Tube

with a Pure Electron Discharge, PHYSICAL REVIEW, 2nd Series 2, No. 6, pp.409-30, December, 1913 (Abstracts in the AMERICAN JOURNAL OF ROENTGENOLOGY 1, No. 3, pp.115-24, January, 1914; GENERAL ELECTRIC REVIEW 17, pp.104-11, February, 1914; ELECTRICAL WORLD 63, pp.220-1, January 24, 1914

Hard X-Rays, THE AMERICAN JOURNAL OF ROENTGENOLOGY 2, No. 6, pp.723-5, April, 1915

A Summary of Physical Investigation Work in Progress on Tubes and Accessories, THE AMERICAN JOURNAL OF ROENTGENOLOGY 2, Nos. 11 and 12, pp.881-92, December, 1915

Roentgen's Discovery. Its Recent Development and Future Possibilities, NEW YORK MEDICAL JOURNAL, December, 1915

Physical Investigation Work in Progress on Tubes and Accessories, THE AMERICAN JOURNAL OF ROENTGENOLOGY 4, No. 2, pp.56–65, February, 1917

Roentgen Rays from Sources other than the Focal Spot in Tubes of the Pure Electron Discharge Type, GENERAL ELECTRIC REVIEW 20, No. 4, pp. 272-81, April 1917; also, Archives of Radiology and Electrotherapy 22, pp.176-83, 216-21, 1917

A New Radiator Type of Hot-Cathode Roentgen-ray Tube, GENERAL ELECTRIC REVIEW 21, No. 1, pp.56-60, January, 1918

A Portable Roentgen-ray Generating Outfit, (with C. N. Moore) GENERAL ELECTRIC REVIEW 21, pp.60-7, January, 1918

The Radiator Type of (X-Ray) Tube, THE AMERICAN JOURNAL OF ROENTGENOLOGY 6, No. 4, pp.175-9, April, 1919

Apparatus for Portable Radiography, JOURNAL OF ROENTGENOLOGY 2, pp.149-76, July, 1919

Oil-immersed X-ray Generating Outfits, THE AMERICAN JOURNAL OF ROENTGENOLOGY 7, No. 4, pp.181-90, April, 1920

A Portable X-ray Outfit, ELECTRICAL WORLD 75, p.981, April, 1920

Tungsten and the Coolidge X-ray Bulbs, ENGINEERING 110, pp.109-10, July, 1920

X-ray Work at Schenectady, JOURNAL OF THE ROENTGEN SOCIETY 17, pp.23-9, January, 1921

The Kearsley Stabilizer, THE AMERICAN JOURNAL OF ROENTGENOLOGY 8, No. 10, pp.599-602, October, 1921

High Voltage X-ray Work, (with W. K. Kearsley) THE AMERICAN JOURNAL OF ROENTGENOLOGY 9, pp.77-101, February, 1922

The Production of X-rays of Short Wave-Length, ALBANY MEDICAL ANNALS, April, 1922

A Water-cooled High-Voltage X-ray Tube, (with C. N. Moore) THE AMERICAN JOURNAL OF ROENTGENOLOGY AND RADIUM THERAPY 10, No. 11, pp.884-90, November, 1923

The Operation of X-ray Tubes at High Voltages, (with C. N. Moore) JOURNAL OF RADIOLOGY 5, No. 1, pp.9-12, January, 1924

Oil-immersed X-ray Generating Outfits and Their Uses, JOURNAL OF THE OPTICAL SOCIETY OF AMERICA; and REVIEW OF SCIENTIFIC INSTRUMENTS 9, pp.653-73, December, 1924; also GENERAL ELECTRIC REVIEW 26, No. 3, pp.182-92, March, 1925

Modern X-ray Tube Development, JOURNAL OF THE FRANKLIN INSTITUTE 199, pp.619-48, May, 1925

High Voltage Cathode Rays Outside the Generating Tube, SCIENCE 62, pp.441-2, November, 1925

The Production of High-Voltage Cathode Rays Outside of the Generating Tube, JOURNAL OF THE FRANKLIN INSTITUTE 202, pp.693-721, December, 1926

Some Experiments with High-Voltage Cathode Rays Outside of the Generating Tube, (with C. N. Moore) JOURNAL OF THE FRANKLIN INSTITUTE 202, pp. 721-34, December, 1926

Effect of High Voltage Cathode Rays on Rickets and on the Activation of Cholesterol, (with A. Knudson) PROCEEDINGS OF THE SOCIETY FOR EXPERIMENTAL BIOLOGY AND MEDICINE 24, pp.366-9, 1927

Some Past Developments and Future Possibilities in Very High Voltage Vacuum Tubes, GENERAL ELECTRIC REVIEW 31, pp.184-5, April, 1928

Cathode-ray and Roentgen-ray Work in Progress, THE AMERICAN JOURNAL OF ROENTGENOLOGY AND RADIUM THERAPY 19, No. 4, pp.313-21, April, 1928

The Development of Modern X-ray Generating Apparatus GENERAL ELECTRIC REVIEW 33, Nos. 11 and 12, pp.608-14, 723-6, November and December, 1930

The Development of Modern Roentgen-ray Generating Apparatus, THE AMERICAN JOURNAL OF ROENTGENOLOGY AND RADIUM THERAPY 24, No. 6, pp.605-20, December, 1930

Hickey, the Scientist, THE AMERICAN JOURNAL OF ROENTGENOLOGY AND RADIUM THERAPY 25, No. 1, pp.170-1, January, 1931

High Voltage Cathode Ray and X-ray Tubes and Their Operation, (with L. E. Dempster and H. E. Tanis, Jr.) PHYSICS 1. No. 4, pp.230-44, October, 1931

A High Voltage Induction Coil and Cascade Tube Roentgen-ray Outfit, (with L. E. Dempster and H. E. Tanis, Jr.) THE AMERICAN JOURNAL OF ROENTGENOLOGY AND RADIUM THERAPY 27, No. 3, pp.495-14, March, 1932

Modern X-ray Tubes, (with E. E. Charlton) Congress International d'Electricite, Paris, Section 10, Rapport No. 2, 14pp., 1932

Experimental Study of Cathode Rays Outside of the Generating Tube. (with C. N. Moore) Congress International d'Electricite, Paris, Section 1, Rapport No. 19, 18pp., 1932; also, GENERAL ELECTRIC REVIEW 35, No. 8, pp.413-17, August, 1932

A Symposium of Some Activities of the Research Laboratory of the General Electric Company — Discussion on X-ray Tubes, (with others) TRANSACTIONS OF THE AMERICAN INSTITUTE OF CHEMICAL ENGINEERS 28, pp.31-55, July, 1933

Roentgen-ray Tubes, (with E. E. Charlton) Chapter 6 of "The Science of Radiology," edited by Otto Glasser and published by

Charles C. Thomas, pp.77-95, 1933

Gas-free Metals Used in X-ray Tubes, (with E. E. Charlton) METAL PROGRESS 24, No. 5, pp. 36-40, November, 1933

Acceptance Address of the Award of Gold Medal by the American Institute of the City of New York to the General Electric Company, GENERAL ELECTRIC REVIEW 37, No. 71, 1943

Scientific Developments and Their Application, THE SCIENTIFIC MONTHLY 38, p.307, 1934

Research as a Career, TECHNOLOGY REVIEW 36, p.341, 1934

Presentation of the Comstock Prize of the National Academy of Sciences to Dr. Ernest Orlando Lawrence, SCIENCE 86, No. 2236, November, 1937

Research in a Large Industry, ARMOUR ENGINEER AND ALUMNUS 3, No. 2, December, 1937

The Production of X-Rays of Very Short Wave Length, RADIOLOGY 30, No. 5, May 1938

Contributions of Physics to Cancer Therapy, (dedication of new building and equipment, Memorial Hospital, New York City) GENERAL ELECTRIC REVIEW 42, No. 7, July, 1939

Elihu Thomson's Interest in Research, SCIENCE 89, No. 2305, March, 1939

Faraday Medal Acceptance Address, ELECTRICAL ENGINEERING 58, No. 6, June, 1939; also GENERAL ELECTRIC REVIEW 42, No. 6, June 1939

X-Rays—Then and Now, ALBANY MEDICAL ANNALS 58, No. 4, December, 1939

Radiation Therapy, RADIOLOGY 34, No. 1, January, 1940

Research and Invention, (presented before the Temporary National Economic Committee, Congress of the United States, 1st session 76th) GOVERNMENT PRINTING OFFICE, 1940

The Research Laboratory of the General Electric Company, SCIENCE 92, No. 2400, December, 1940

Seventy Years of Physical Science, POPULAR SCIENCE MONTHLY 140, No. 5, May, 1942

The Role of Science Institutions in our Civilization, SCIENCE 96, No. 2497, November, 1942

Response in Accepting the Duddell Medal at the Meeting of the American Physical Society, JOURNAL OF APPLIED PHYSICS 13, No. 8, August, 1942

Peacetime Salvage from Wartime Research, *Address given before the Dental Society of the State of New York,* 1943

The Rapidly Expanding Field of Usefulness of X-Rays, JOURNAL OF THE FRANKLIN INSTITUTE 237, No. 6, June, 1944

Roentgen Rays: Tubes, (Dr. Coolidge, Z. J, Atlee) MEDICAL PHYSICS, edited by Otto Glasser, Chicago, 1944

Roentgen-Ray Tubes (with E. E. Charlton) RADIOLOGY 45, No. 5, November, 1945

Experiences with the Roentgen-Ray Tube, THE AMERICAN JOURNAL OF ROENTGENOLOGY AND RADIUM THERAPY 54, No. 6, December 1945

Highlights of the Past and a Challenge for the Future, X-RAY TECHNICIAN 20, January, 1949

My Early Work in Tungsten, *Remarks on receiving Li Medal,* May, 1952

A plea for More Fundamental Research Effort, SCIENCE 119, No. 3082, January, 1945

A Half Century's Development of X-Ray Generators, AMERICAN JOURNAL OF ROENTGENOLOGY, RADIUM THERAPY AND NUCLEAR MEDICINE 75, No. 1, January 1956

Patents Issued to William David Coolidge

935463	1909	Dies and Die Supports
963872	1910	Lamp-Filaments
1004557	1911	Resistance-Furnaces
1008588	1911	Filaments
1010866	1911	Process of Making Composite Conductors
1026343	1912	The Manufacture of Refractory Conductors
1026344	1912	Binders for the Manufacture of Refractory Conductors
1026345	1912	Apparatus for Treating Filaments
1026382	1912	Metal Filaments
1026383	1912	Metal Filaments
1026384	1912	Metal Filaments
1026428	1912	Tungsten Purification
1026429	1912	Refractory Conductors
1047502	1912	The Art of Manufacturing Lamp Filaments
1077674	1913	The Production of Refractory Conductors
1082933	1913	Ductile Tungsten
1089907	1914	Electrical Contacts
1096414	1914	Electric Furnaces
1101062	1914	Methods of Joining Unlike Metals
1153290	1915	X-Ray Targets
1157925	1915	Vacuum-Tube Electrodes and Processes of Operating
1162339	1915	Methods of Making Composite Metal Bodies
1162340	1915	Methods of Uniting Metals
1162341	1915	Composite Metal Bodies
1162342	1915	Composite Metal Bodies
1181741	1916	Methods of Joining Metals
1181742	1916	Electrical Contacts
1203495	1916	Vacuum Tubes
1211091	1917	Cathode-Ray Devices
1211092	1917	X-Ray Tubes
1211376	1917	Electron-Discharge Apparatus
1215116	1917	X-Ray Apparatus
1226470	1917	Refractory-Metal Tubes
1226471	1917	Refractory-Metal Tubes
1230869	1917	Methods of Making Incandescent Lamps
1250093	1917	Stereoscopic X-Ray Apparatus
1253156	1918	Roentgen-Ray Devices
1261708	1918	Electron-Discharge Devices
1268685	1918	Electric-Resistance Furnaces
1289672	1918	Methods of Producing & Maintaining Vacuums
1310061	1919	X-Ray Apparatus

Citations

for

Medals and Awards

1914 *Rumford Medal*
of the American Academy of Arts and
Science
for his invention of ductile tungsten.

1926 *Howard N. Potts Medal*
of the Franklin Institute
in consideration of the originality and ingenuity
shown in the development of a vacuum tube that
has simplified and revolutionized the production
of x-rays.

1926 *Louis Edward Levy Gold Medal*
of the Franklin Institute
for his paper on "The Production of High Voltage Cathode Rays Outside the Generating Tube."

1927 *Gold Medal*
of the American College of Radiology
in recognition of his contribution to radiology and
the science of medicine.

1927 *Hughes Medal*
of the Royal Society, London
for his work on the x-rays and the development of
highly efficient apparatus for their production.

1927 *Edison Medal*
of the American Institute of Electrical
Engineers
for his contributions to the incandescent electric
lighting and the x-ray arts.

1932 *Washington Award*
of the Western Society of Engineers
in recognition of devoted, unselfish, and preeminent service in advancing human progress.

1937 *John Scott Award*
granted by the City Trusts of the City of
Philadelphia.
Based on his application of a new principle in
x-ray tubes.

1939 *Faraday Medal*
of the Institution of Electrical Engineers
of England
for notable scientific or industrial achievement in
Electrical Engineering.

1940 *Modern Pioneer Award*
of the National Manufacturer's Association
awarded to Dr. Coolidge as "A Modern Pioneer."

1942 *Duddell Medal*
(18th) of the Physical Society of England
in recognition of his invention of the Coolidge
x-ray tube.

1942 *Orden al Merito*
of the Chilean Government
for his many services to civilization.

1944 *Franklin Medal*
of the Franklin Institute
in recognition of his contributions to the welfare
of humanity, especially in the field of the manufacture of ductile tungsten and in the field of improved apparatus for the production and control
of x-rays.

1952 *K. C. Li Medal and Award*
First recipient—Columbia University
for meritorius achievement in advancing the science of tungsten.

1953 *Henry Spenadel Award*
of the First District Dental Society
for Distinguished and Significant contributions to
dentistry.

1963 *Roentgen Medal*
of the Society of the Friends of the German
Roentgen Museum
to individuals of Germany and other countries
who have helped in the advancement and dissemination of Roentgen's discovery in both the scientific and practical aspects; or who have been of
especial service to the German Roentgen Museum.

Honorary Degrees

••

Union College, June 1927
Doctor of Science

Lehigh University, June 1927
Doctor of Science

University of Zurich, September 1937
Doctor of Medicine

Ursinus College, October 13, 1942
Doctor of Laws

University of Sao Paulo, November 1945
Doctor "Honoris Causa"

National School of Engineering
University of Brazil, November 1945
Doctor "Honoris Causa"

Catholic University of Chile, November 1945
Doctor of Science

Indiana Technical College, May 1947
Doctor of Engineering

205

Society Memberships

National Academy of Sciences
American Academy of Arts and Sciences
Washington Academy of Science (V. Pres. 1931)
American Association for the Advancement of Science
American Chemical Society (Emeritus Status)
American Electrochemical Society
American Institute of Electrical Engineers (Fellow)
American Physical Society
American Inst. Chemists
Sigma Xi
American Philosophical Society
Edison Pioneers
Eta Kappa Nu (Eminent Member)

Honorary Memberships

The American Roentgen Ray Society
The American Radium Society
The Radiological Society of North America
American College of Radiology
The Roentgen Society, of England
Société de Radiologie Medicale, de France
Nordisk Förening för Medicinsk Radiologi, Scandinavia
The Pan-American Medical Association
Societe Francaise des Electriciens
Medical Society of the County of Schenectady
The Dental Society of the State of New York
The Franklin Institute
Brazilian Institute for Study of Tuberculosis
Brazilian Society of Medical Radiology

Paulista Medical Association
Chilean Society of Radiology
Faculty of Physical and Mathematical Sciences of the University
of Chile
Faculty of Biological and Medical Sciences of the University
of Chile
Argentine Electrotechnical Association
Sociedad Peruana De Radiologia
Sociedad Argentina de Radiologia

Corresponding Memberships

Brazilian Academy of Science
National Academy of Exact Physical and Natural Sciences of
Lima
Société Française des Électriciens

Acknowledgements

In the collection of information for this story of William David Coolidge the author was fortunate in having the assistance of many friends and associates of the distinguished scientist. Grateful acknowledgement is made of the assistance they have given. In particular the author wishes to acknowledge the help of members of the staff of the General Electric Research Laboratory and the X-Ray Department of the General Electric Company, as well as the courtesy of the American Roentgen Ray Society and the American Institute of Electrical Engineers for permission to quote from their publications. But to Dr. Coolidge, himself, more than to all others, the author's thanks are due for his making available a large volume of his personal notes and memoranda, and for his untiring willingness to verify facts and dates pertaining to the story.

John A. Miller

INDEX

RL indicates Research Laboratory

5/25/27 Frid. Dr W. has asked me
Have started Lenard & Hot
electrodes with butt contac
whether, with close spacing t
haust, by cold cath. disch.

5/9/27 Last Fri. & Sat., Dr Crocker of Bo

5/24/27 In Wash. & Phila. last wk. gettin

6/20/27 The Tripps left this morning,

6/27/27 Mr. Rice in — showed him the

6/28/27 " " & Mr. Dow in to see
700 KV operation, with 0.5 m.a
With D, went out to R.P. at 5 P.M.
& Phila. He sent us up in one

6/29/27 Ass't Sec'y of Navy, Warner, & sis
in the Ford plane & she left in her

		u.f	amps	m.a.
600° primary		3.7	10.5	0.5

7/14/27 Back last night _____ 0.45
from Camp Gen'l. W. & Page r